MW00535152

ANIMAL ANATOMY COLORING BOOK

SCAN THE CODE TO ACCESS YOUR FREE DIGITAL COPY

THIS BOOK BELONGS TO

TABLE OF CONTENTS

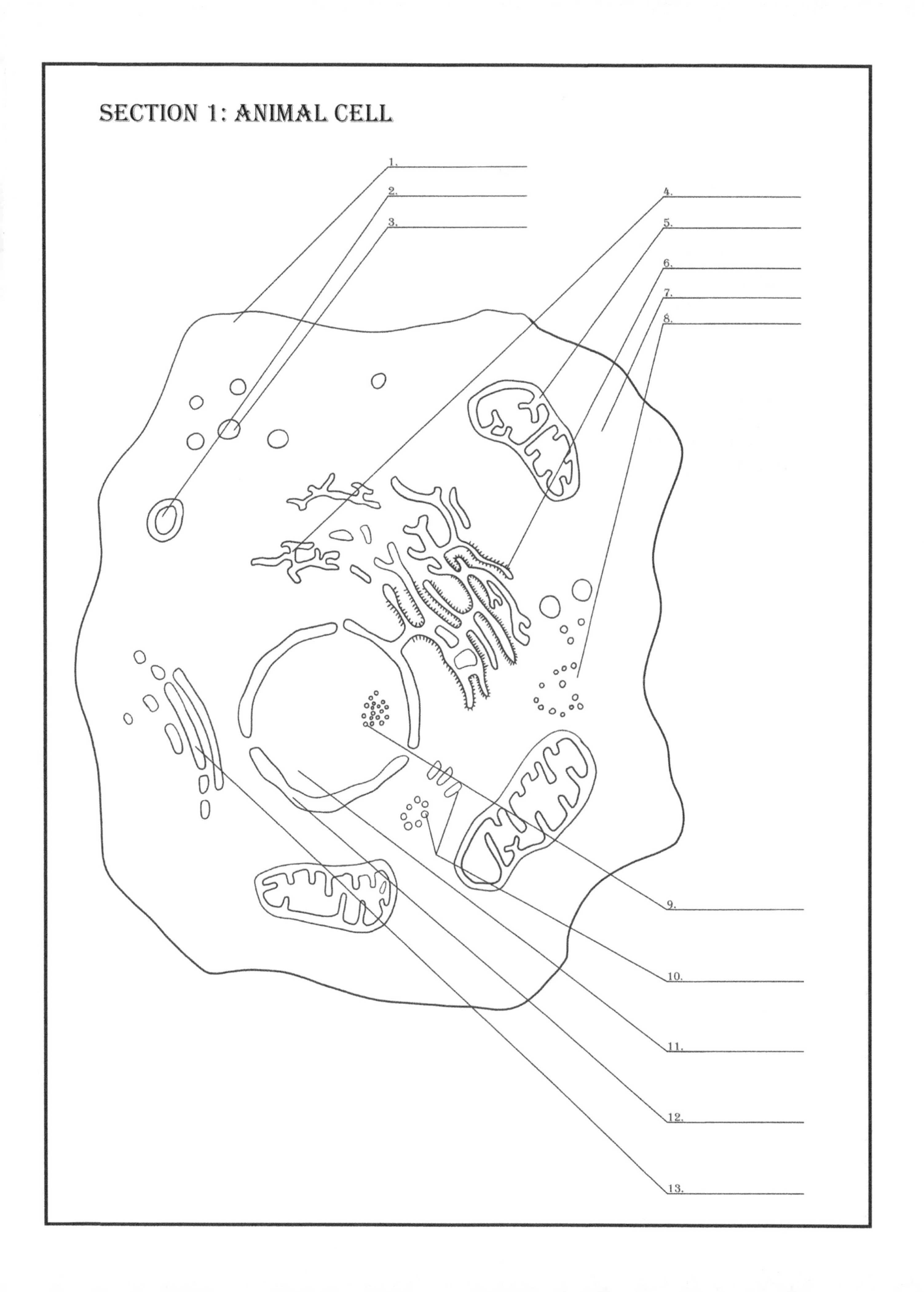
SECTION 1: ANIMAL CELL
1.
2.
3.
4.
5.
6.
7.
8.
9.
10.
11.
12.
13.

SECTION 1: ANIMAL CELL

1. CELL MEMBRANE
2. LYSOSOME
3. VACUOLE
4. SMOOTH ENDOPLASMIC RETICULUM
5. MITOCHONDRION
6. ROUGH ENDOPLASMIC RETICULUM
7. CYTOPLASM
8.RIBOSOME
9. NUCLEOLUS
10. CETNRIOLES
11. CHROMATIN
12. NUCLEAR MEMBRANE
13. GOLGI APPARATUS

SECTION 2: FISH EXTERNAL FORM AND INTERNAL STRUCTURE

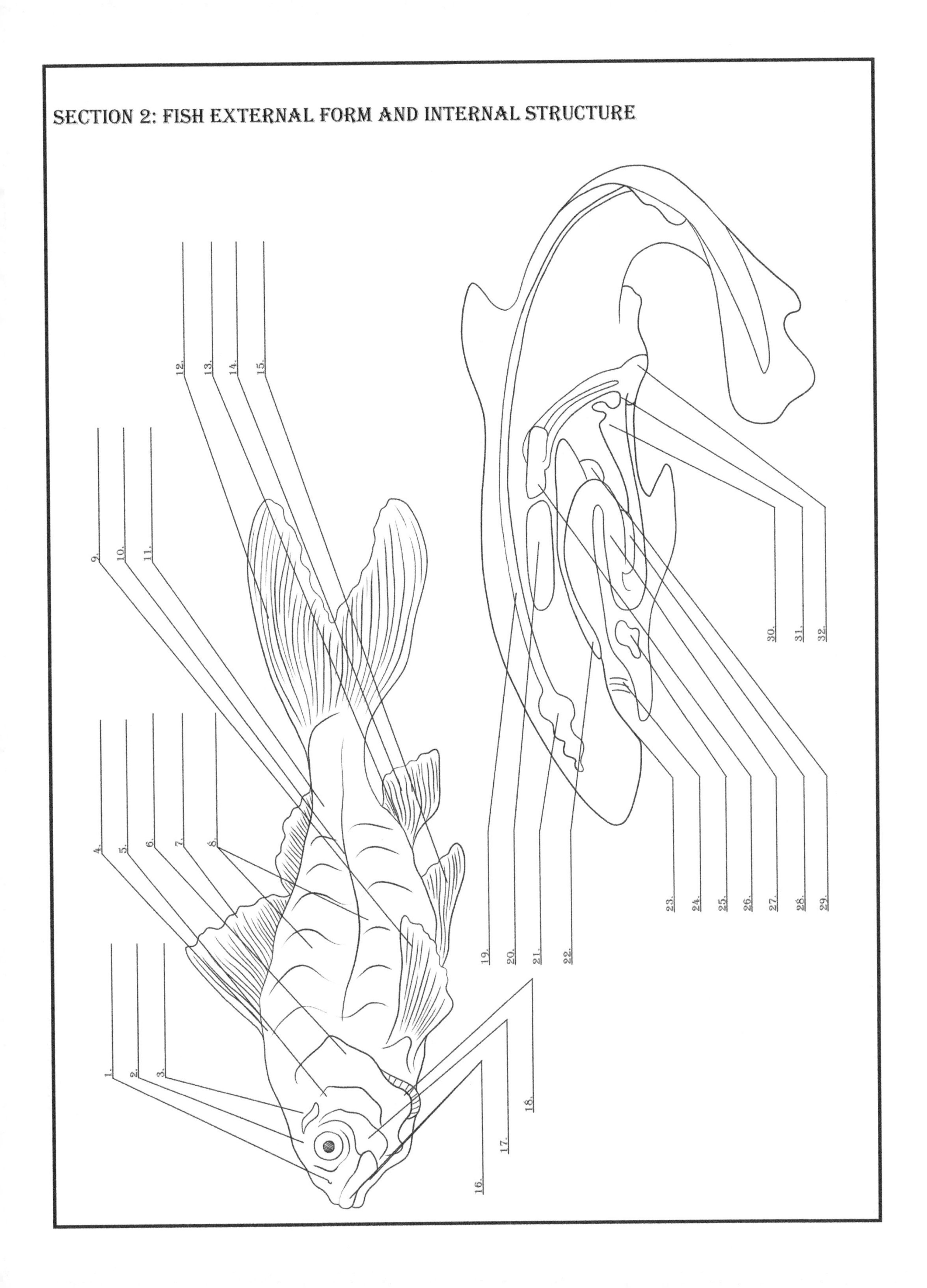

SECTION 2: FISH EXTERNAL FORM AND INTERNAL STRUCTURE

1. NOSTRIL
2. EYE
3. LEVATOR OCULI MUSCLE
4. DORSALIS MUSCLE
5. PREOPERCULUM
6. OPERCULUM (GIL COVER)
7. DORSAL FIN (ANTERIOR)
8. MYOTOME MUSCLES
9. PECTORAL FIN
10.LATERAL LINE
11.HORIZONTAL SEPTUM
12.CAUDAL FIN
13.ANUS
14.ANAL FIN
15. PELVIC FIN
16.MAXILLA
17.ABDUCTOR MANDIBULAE
18. BRACHIOSTEGALS
19.SPINAł CORD
20.OVARY
21.BRAIN
22.LIVER
23.MOUTH
24.GILL SLIT
25. HEART
26.KIDNEY
27. STOMACH
28.PANCREAS
29.SPLEEN
30.INTESTINE
31.RECTUM
32.CLOACA

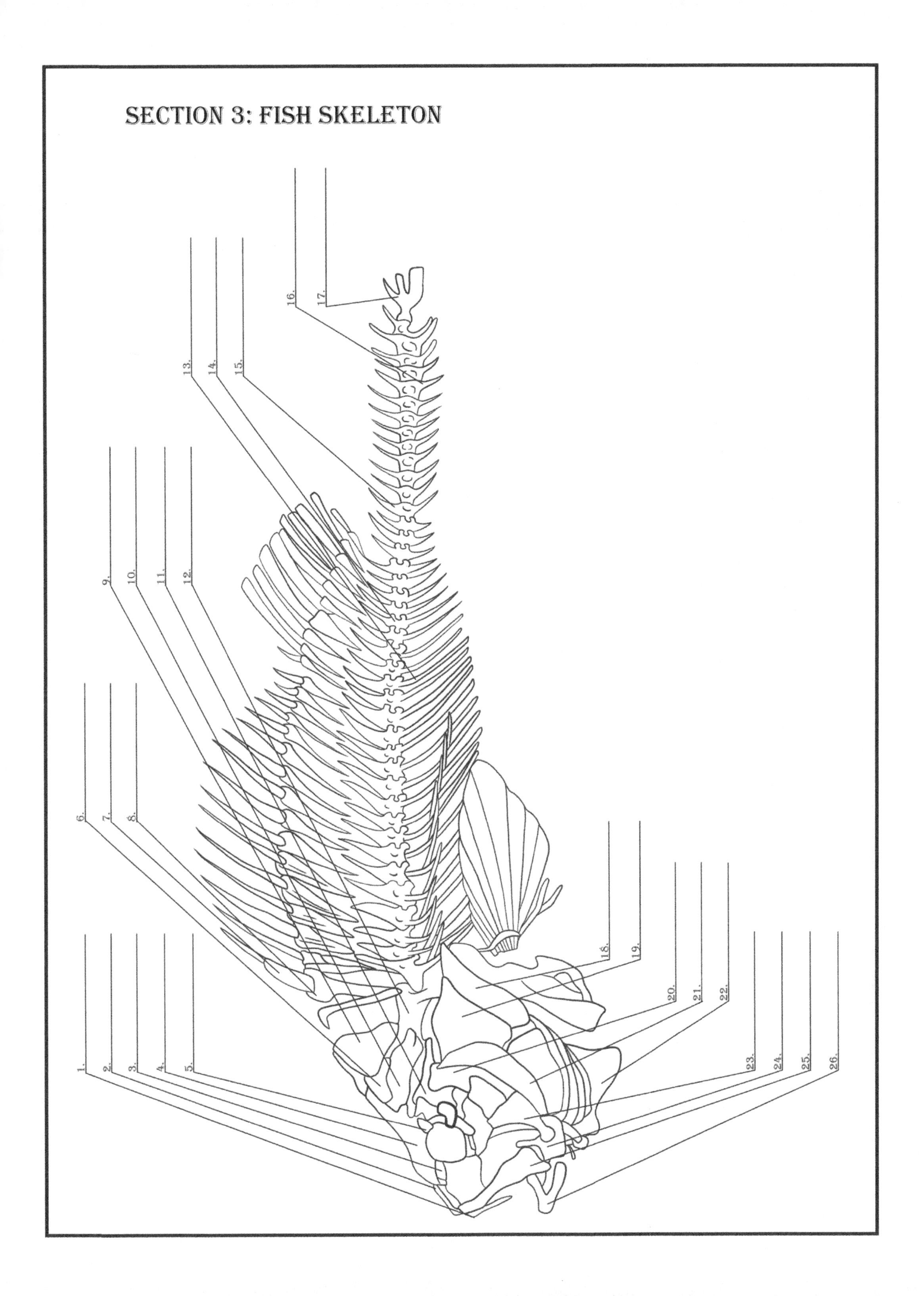
SECTION 3: FISH SKELETON
1.
2.
3.
4.
5.
6.
7.
8.
9.
10.
11.
12.
13.
14.
15.
16.
17.
18.
19.
20.
21.
22.
23.
24.
25.
26.

SECTION 3: FISH SKELETON

1. PREMAXILLA
2. ETHMOID
3. PREFRONTAL BONE
4. FRONTAL BONE
5. POSTFRONTAL BONE
6. PARIETAL BONE
7. DERMAL FIN RAY
8. BASAL AND RADIAL CARTILAGES
9. SUPRAOCCIPITAL BONE
10. EPIOTIC BONE
11. SQUAMOSAL BONE
12. PRETOTIC BONE
13. RIB
14. VERTEBRA
15. NEUTRAL SPINE
16. HEMAL SPINE
17. NOTOCHORD
18. SUBOPERCULAR BONE
19. OPERCULAR BONE
20. HYOMANDIBULAR BONE
21. PREOPERCULAR BONE
22. UROHYAL
23. QUADRATE BONE
24. ARTICULAR BONE
25. MAXILLA
26. DENARY BONE

SECTION 4: FROG EXTERNAL AND INTERNAL FORM

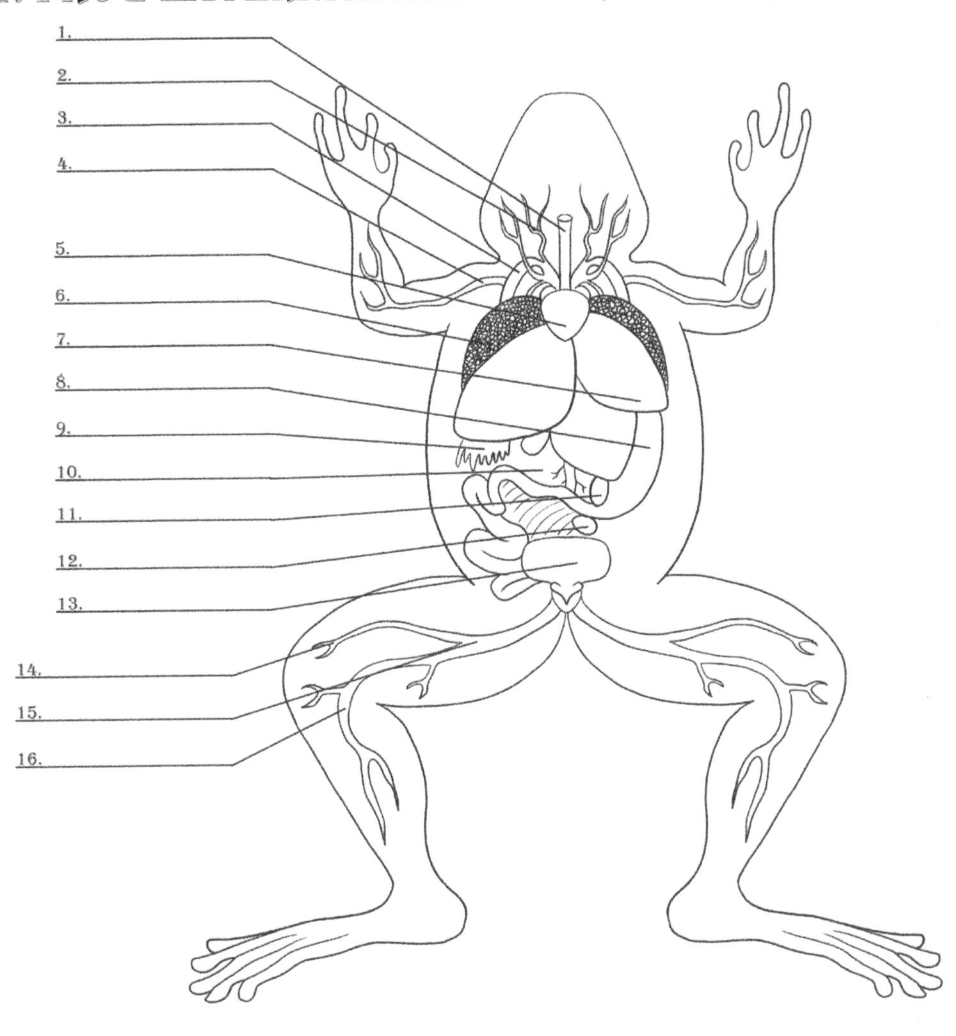

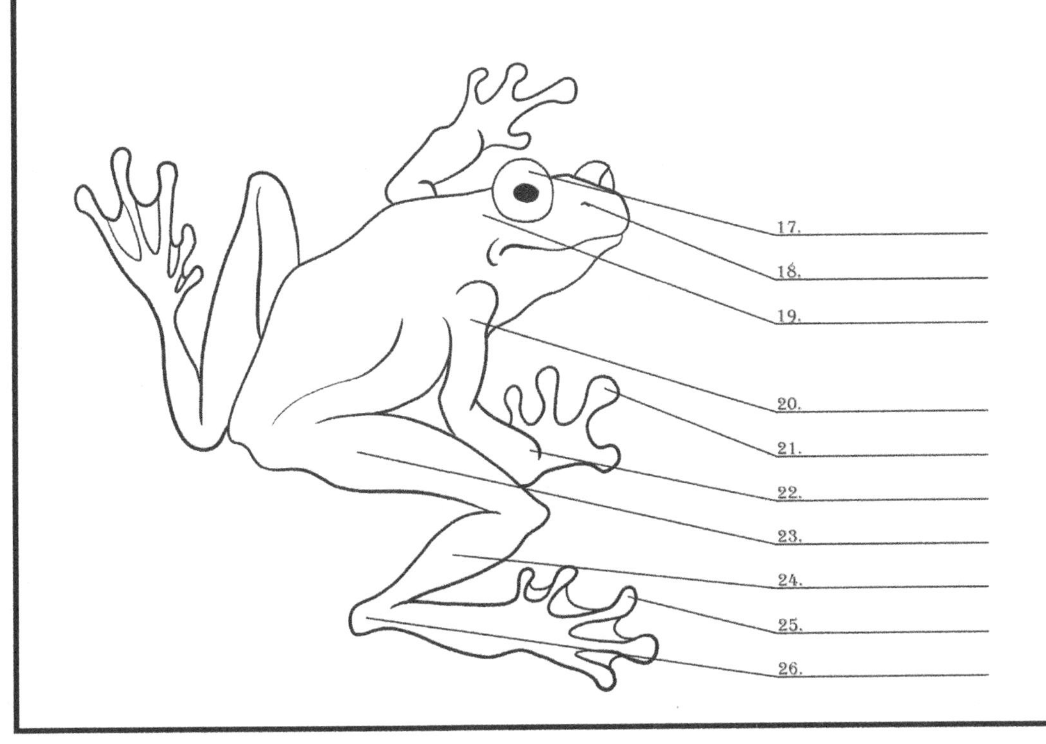

SECTION 4: FROG EXTERNAL AND INTERNAL FORM

1. ESOPHAGUS
2. CAROTID ARTERY
3. AORTIC ARCH
4. SUBCLAVIAN ARTERY
5. HEART
6. LUNGS
7. LIVER
8. STOMACH
9. FAT BODIES
10. KIDNEY
11. PANCREAS
12. SPLEEN
13. BLADDER
14. FEMORAL ARTERY
15. COMMON ILIAC ARTERY
16. SCIATIC ARTERY
17. EYE
18. EXTERNAL NOSTRIL
19. EAR DRUM
20. UPPER ARM
21. FINGER
22. WRIST
23. THIGH
24. SHANK
25. WEBBED TOE
26. ANKLE

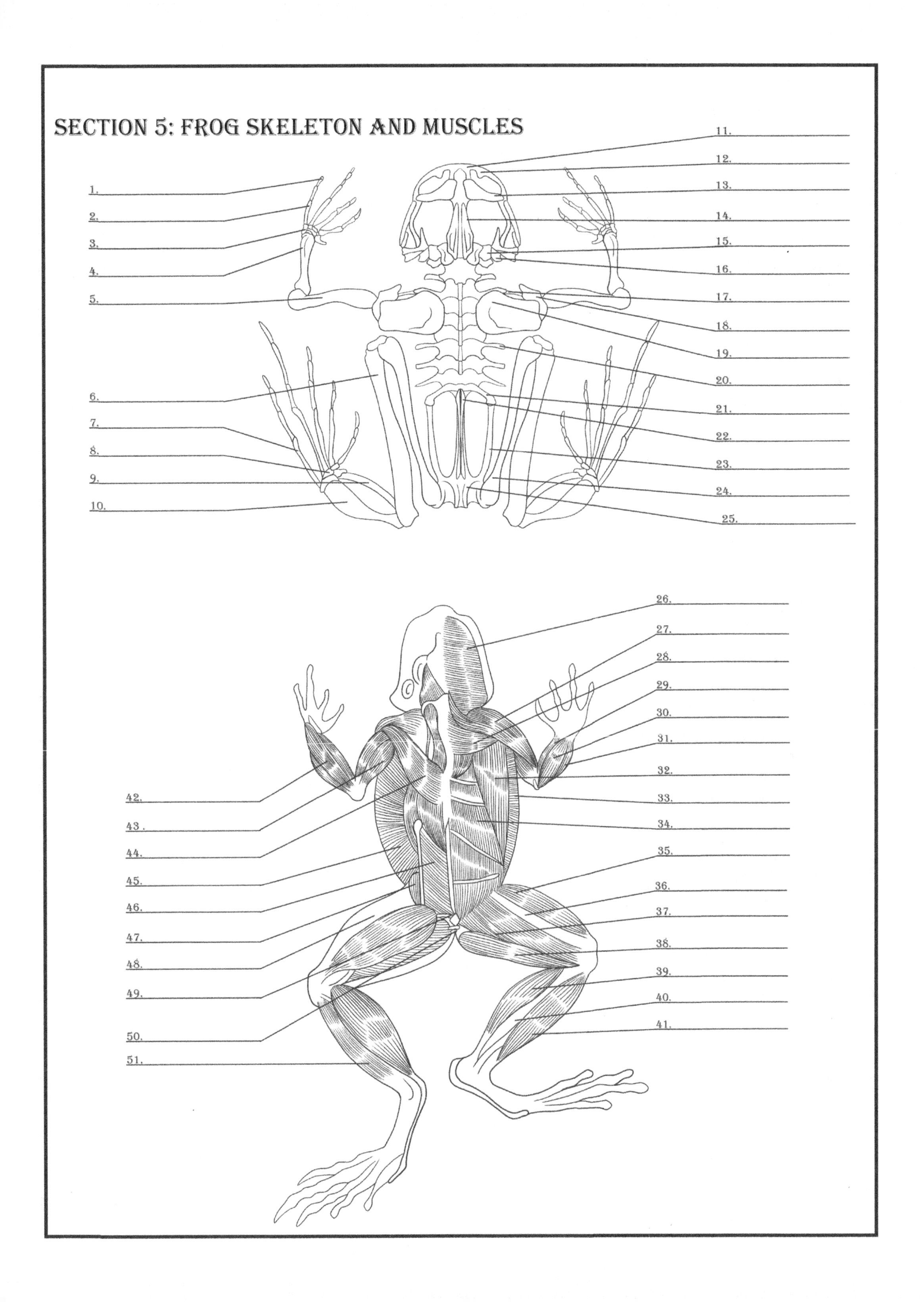
SECTION 5: FROG SKELETON AND MUSCLES
1.
2.
3.
4.
5.
6.
7.
8.
9.
10.
11.
12.
13.
14.
15.
16.
17.
18.
19.
20.
21.
22.
23.
24.
25.
26.
27.
28.
29.
30.
31.
32.
33.
34.
35.
36.
37.
38.
39.
40.
41.
42.
43.
44.
45.
46.
47.
48.
49.
50.
51.

SECTION 5: FROG SKELETON AND MUSCLES

1. PHALANGE
2. METACARPAL
3. CARPAL
4. RADIOULNA
5. HUMERUS
6. TIBIOFIBULA
7. METATARSAL
8. TARSAL
9. ASTRALAGUS
10. CALCANEUM
11. PREMAXILLA
12. MAXILLA
13. NASAL BONE
14. FRONTOPARIETAL BONE
15. PROOTIC BONE
16. EXOCCIPITAL BONE
17. CLAVICLE
18. CORACOID
19. SUPRASCAPULA
20. VERTEBRA
21. SACRAL VERTEBRA
22. UROSTYLE
23. ILIUM
24. FEMUR
25. ISCHIUM
26. MYLOHYOID
27. CORACORDIALIS
28. DELTOID
29. FLEXOR CARPI RADIALIS
30. FLEXOR PALMARIS
31. FLEXOR CARPI ULNARIS
32. PECTORALIS
33. OBLIQUUS EXTERNUS
34. RECTUS ABDOMINIS
35. TRICEPS FEMORIS
36. ABDUCTOR LONGUS
37. ABDUCTOR MAGNUS
38. GRACILIS MINOR
39. GASTROCNEMICUS
40. TIBIALIS POSTICUS
41. TIBIALIS ANTICUS LONGUS
42. DORSALISSCAPULAE
43. TRICEPS BRACHII
44. LATISSIMUS DORSI
45. OBLIQUUS INTERNUS
46. COCCYGEOILIACUS
47. ILIACUS EXTERNUS
48. ILIACUS
49. PYRIFORMIS
50. ANUS
51. PERONEUS

SECTION 6: LIZARD SKELETON AND INTERNAL STRUCTURE

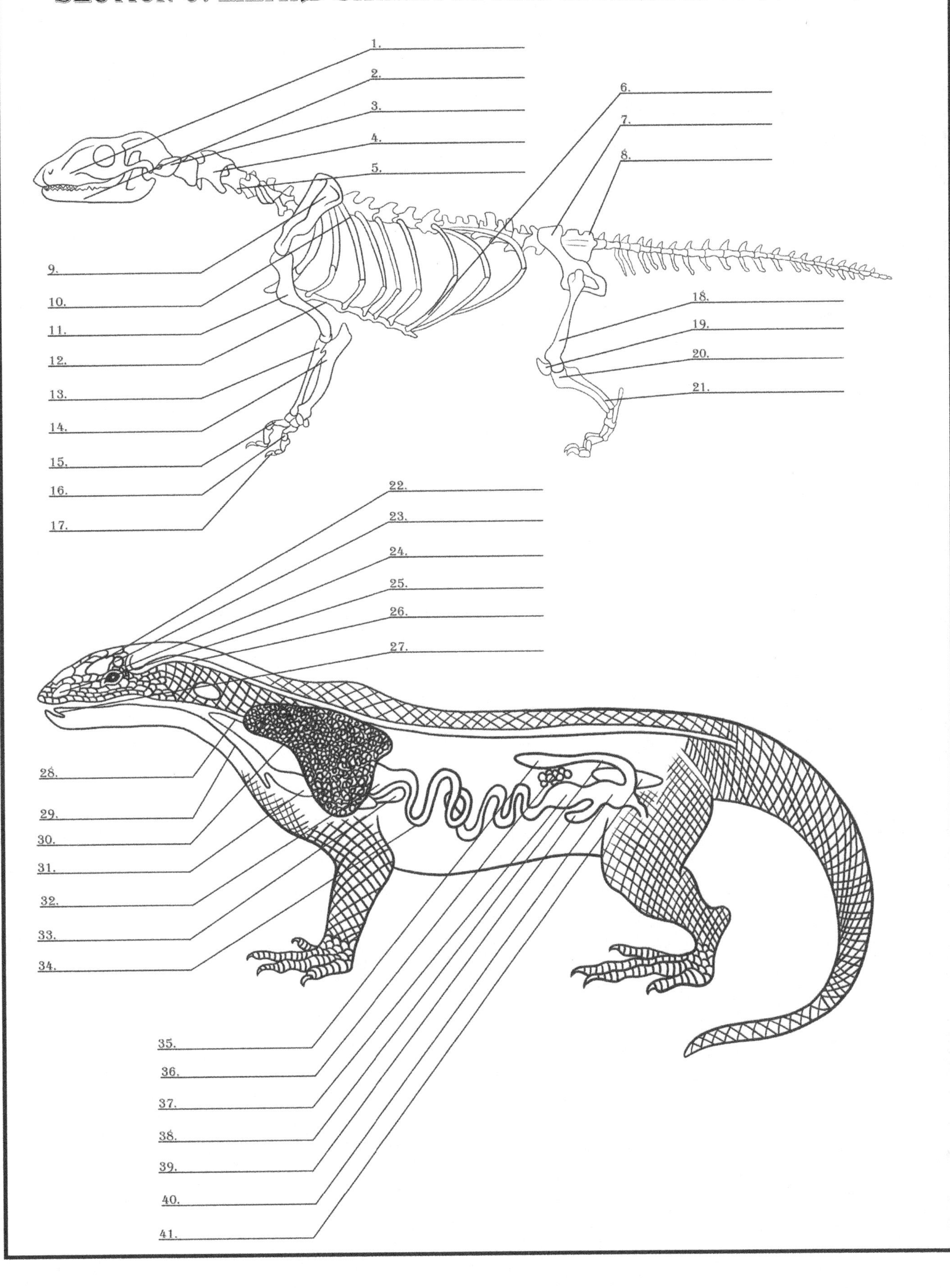

SECTION 6: LIZARD SKELETON AND INTERNAL STRUCTURE

1. SKULL
2. MANDIBLE
3. ATLAS
4. AXIS
5. CERVICAL VERTEBRAE
6. COSTAL CARTILAGE
7. PELVIS
8. SACRUM
9. SCAPULA
10. RIB
11. HUMERUS
12. STERNUM
13. RADIUS
14. ULNA
15. METACARPAL
16. PHALANGE
17. CLAW
18. FEMUR
19. PATELLA
20. TIBIA
21. FIBULA
22. CEREBRUM
23. OPTIC LOBE
24. CEREBELLUM
25. NOSTRIL
26. SPINAL CORD
27. TONGUE
28. TRACHEA
29. ESOPHAGUS
30. LIVER
31. LUNG
32. STOMACH
33. PANCREAS
34. DUODENUM
35. FUNNEL
36. OVARY
37. RECTUM
38. OVIDUCT
39. BLADDER
40. CLOACA
41. KIDNEY

SECTION 7: LIZARD MUSCLES

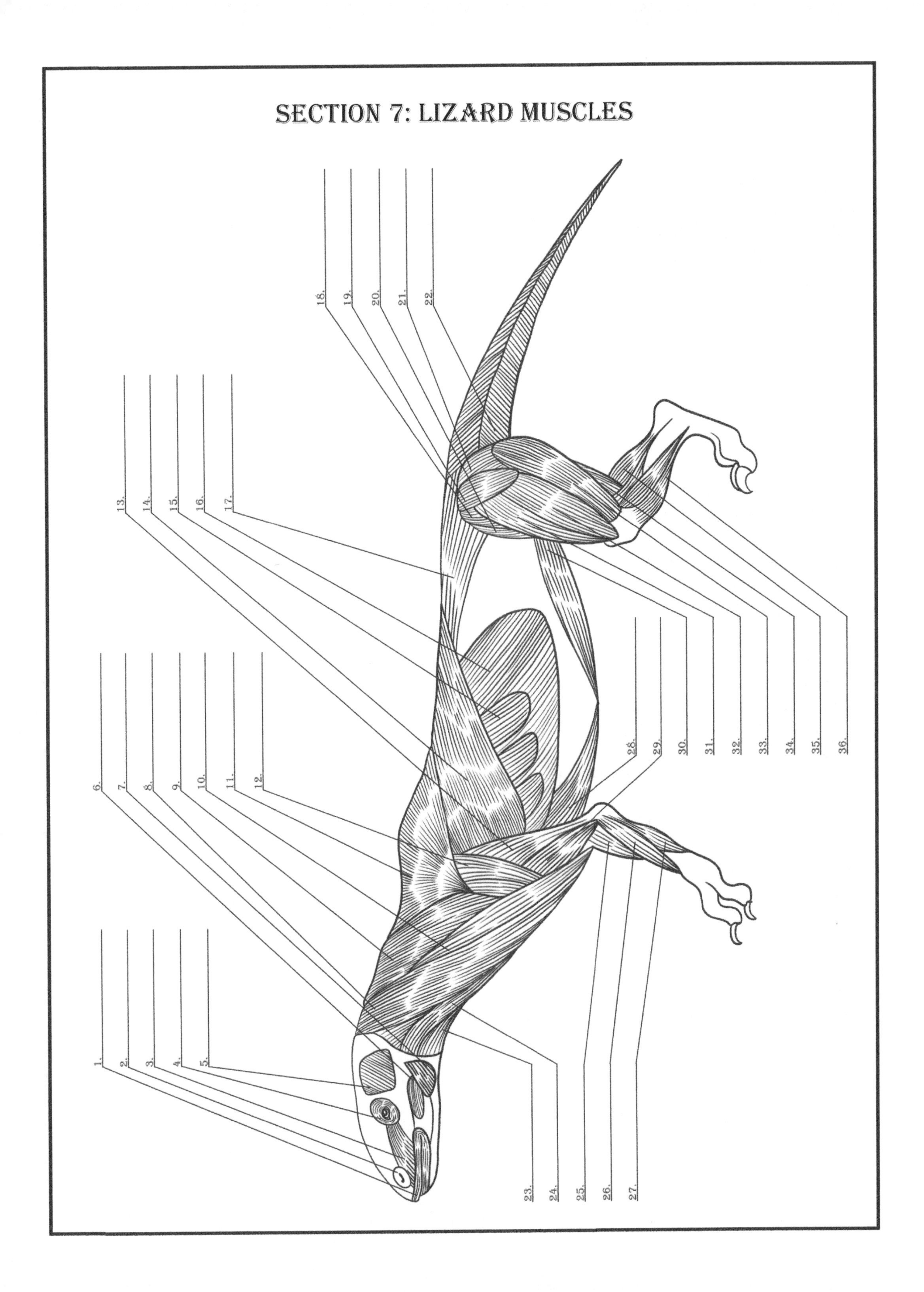

SECTION 7: LIZARD MUSCLES

1. ORBICULARIS ORIS
2. NOSTRIL
3. LEVATOR NASOLABIALIS
4. ORBICULARIS OCCULI
5. TEMPORALIS
6. ZYGOMATICUS
7. MASSETER
8. BRACHIOCEPUHALICUS
9. SPLENIUS
10. OMOTRANSVERSARIUS
11. TRAPEZIUS
12. DELTOID
13. TRICEPS
14. LATISSIMUS DORSI
15. SERRATUS VENTRALIS THORACIS
16. EXTERNAL ABDOMINAL OBLIQUE
17. LONGISSIMUS DORSI
18. RECTUS FEMORIS
19. GLUTEUS MEDIUS
20. SARTORIUS
21. GLUTEUS SUPERFICIAL
22. COCCYGEUS
23. STERNOTHYROHYOID
24. STERNOMANDIBULARIW
25. BRACHIORADIALIS
26. EXTENSOR DIGITORUM COMMUNIS
27. ULNARIS LATERALIS
28. PECTORALIS ASCENDENS
29. BRACHIALIS
30. RECTUS ABDOMINALIS
31. TENSOR FASCIALATAE
32. VASTUS LATRANS
33. BICEPS FEMORIS
34. SEMITENDINOSUS
35. GASTROCNEMICUS
36. EXTENSOR LATERALIS

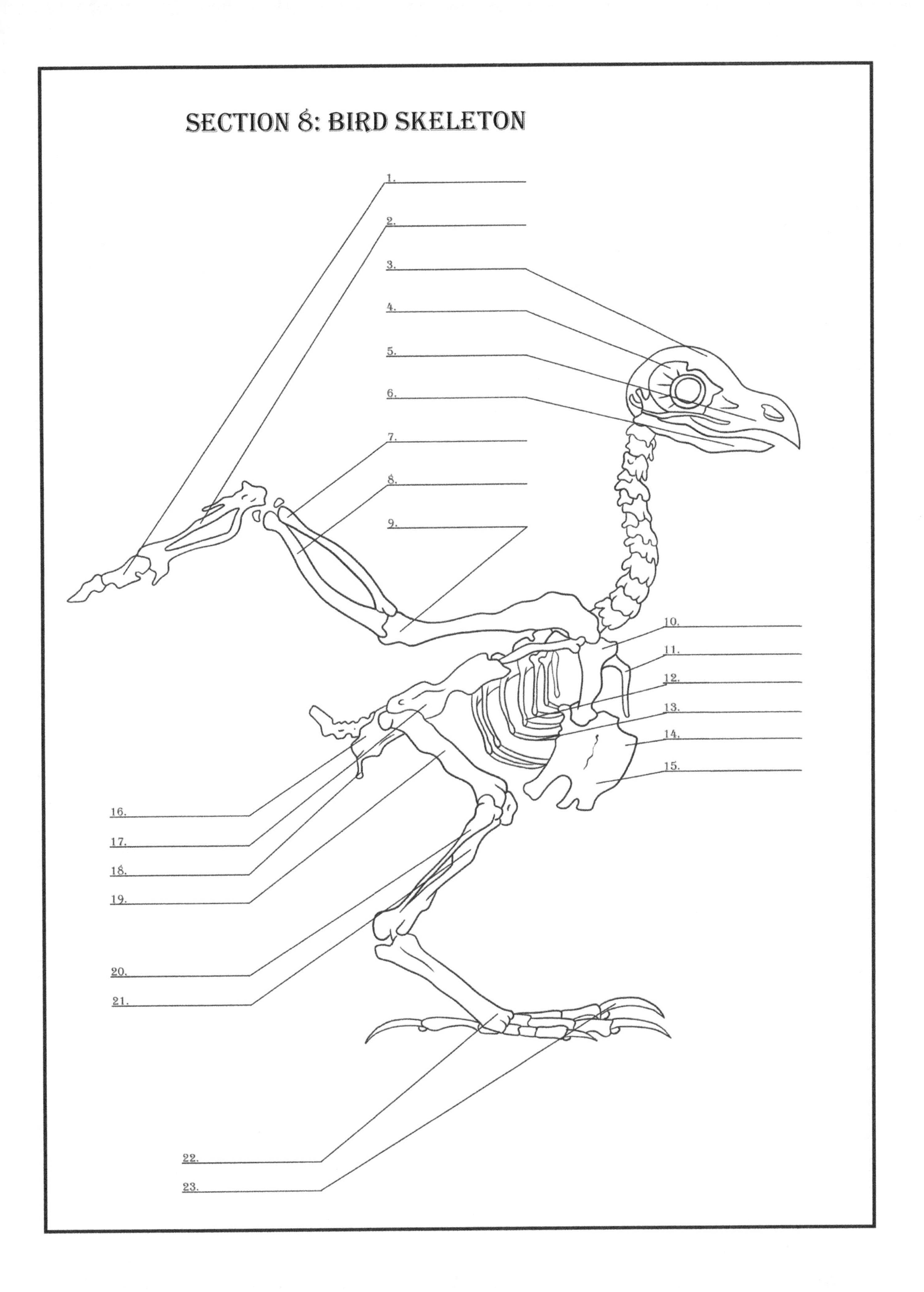
SECTION 8: BIRD SKELETON
1.
2.
3.
4.
5.
6.
7.
8.
9.
10.
11.
12.
13.
14.
15.
16.
17.
18.
19.
20.
21.
22.
23.

SECTION 8: BIRD SKELETON

1. PHALANGE
2. METACARPAL
3. CRANIUM
4. SCLERAL BONE (EYE SOCKET)
5. UPPER MANDIBLE
6. LOWER MANDIBLE
7. RADIUS
8. ULNA
9. HUMERUS
10. CORACOID
11. WURCULA (WISH BONEO
12. RIB
13. STERNAL RIB
14. KEEL
15. STERNUM
16. ISCHIUM
17. ILIUM
18. PUBIS
19. FEMUR
20. FIBULA
21. TIBIA
22. TARSOMETATARSUS
23. DIGIT

SECTION 9: BIRD INTERNAL STRUCTURE

1. ____
2. ____
3. ____
4. ____
5. ____
6. ____
7. ____
8. ____
9. ____
10. ____
11. ____
12. ____
13. ____
14. ____
15. ____
16. ____
17. ____
18. ____
19. ____
20. ____
21. ____
22. ____
23. ____
24. ____
25. ____
26. ____
27. ____
28. ____
29. ____
30. ____
31. ____
32. ____
33. ____
34. ____

SECTION 9: BIRD INTERNAL STRUCTURE

1. CEREBRUM
2. CEREBELLUM
3. SPINAL CORD
4. ESOPHAGUS
5. TRACHEA
6. KIDNEY
7. AIR SAC
8. STOMACH
9. GLIZZARD
10. INTESTINE
11. CLOACA
12. CROP
13. LUNG
14. LIVER
15. COMB
16. BRAIN
17. BEAK
18. ESOPHAGUS
19. TRACHEA
20. SPINAL CORD
21. OVARY
22. KIDNEY
23. OVIDUCT
24. CLOACA
25. LUNG
26. CROP
27. HEART
28. PROVENTRICULUS
29. GALL BLADDER
30. SPLEEN
31. GLIZZARD
32. MESENTERY
33. DUODENAL LOOP
34. PANCREAS

SECTION 10: BIRD EXTERNAL STRUCTURE

1. ______________
2. ______________
3. ______________
4. ______________
5. ______________
6. ______________
7. ______________
8. ______________
9. ______________
10. ______________
11. ______________
12. ______________
13. ______________
14. ______________
15. ______________
16. ______________
17. ______________
18. ______________
19. ______________
20. ______________
21. ______________
22. ______________
23. ______________
24. ______________
25. ______________
26. ______________
27. ______________
28. ______________
29. ______________
30. ______________
31. ______________
32. ______________
33. ______________
34. ______________
35. ______________
36. ______________
37. ______________
38. ______________
39. ______________
40. ______________
41. ______________
42. ______________

SECTION 10: BIRD EXTERNAL STRUCTURE

1. NAPE
2. CROWN
3. THROAT
4. MALAR
5. LESSER SECONDARY COVERTS
6. MEDIAN SECONDARY COVERTS
7. ALULA
8. GREATER SECONDARY COVERTS
9. PRIMARY COVERTS
10. MANTLE
11. SCAPULARS
12. TERTIALS
13. RUMP
14. UPPER TAIL COVERTS
15. TAIL
16. FOREHEAD
17. EYEBROW STRIPE
18. CROWN
19. EYE RING
20. EAR COVERTS
21. NAPE
22. BACK
23. UPPER MANDIBLE
24. NOSTRIL
25. LOWER MANDIBLE
26. LORE
27. BREAST
28. FLANK
29. TIBIA
30. TARSUS
31. FOOT
32. CLAW
33. RUMP
34. PRIMARY WING FEATHERS
35. UPPER TAIL COVERTS
36. UNDERTAIL COVERTS
37. TAIL
38. RACHIS
39. VANE
40. AFTERFEATHER
41. DOWNY BARBS
42. HOLLOW SHAFT

SECTION 11: RAT SKELETON AND INTERNAL STRUCTURE

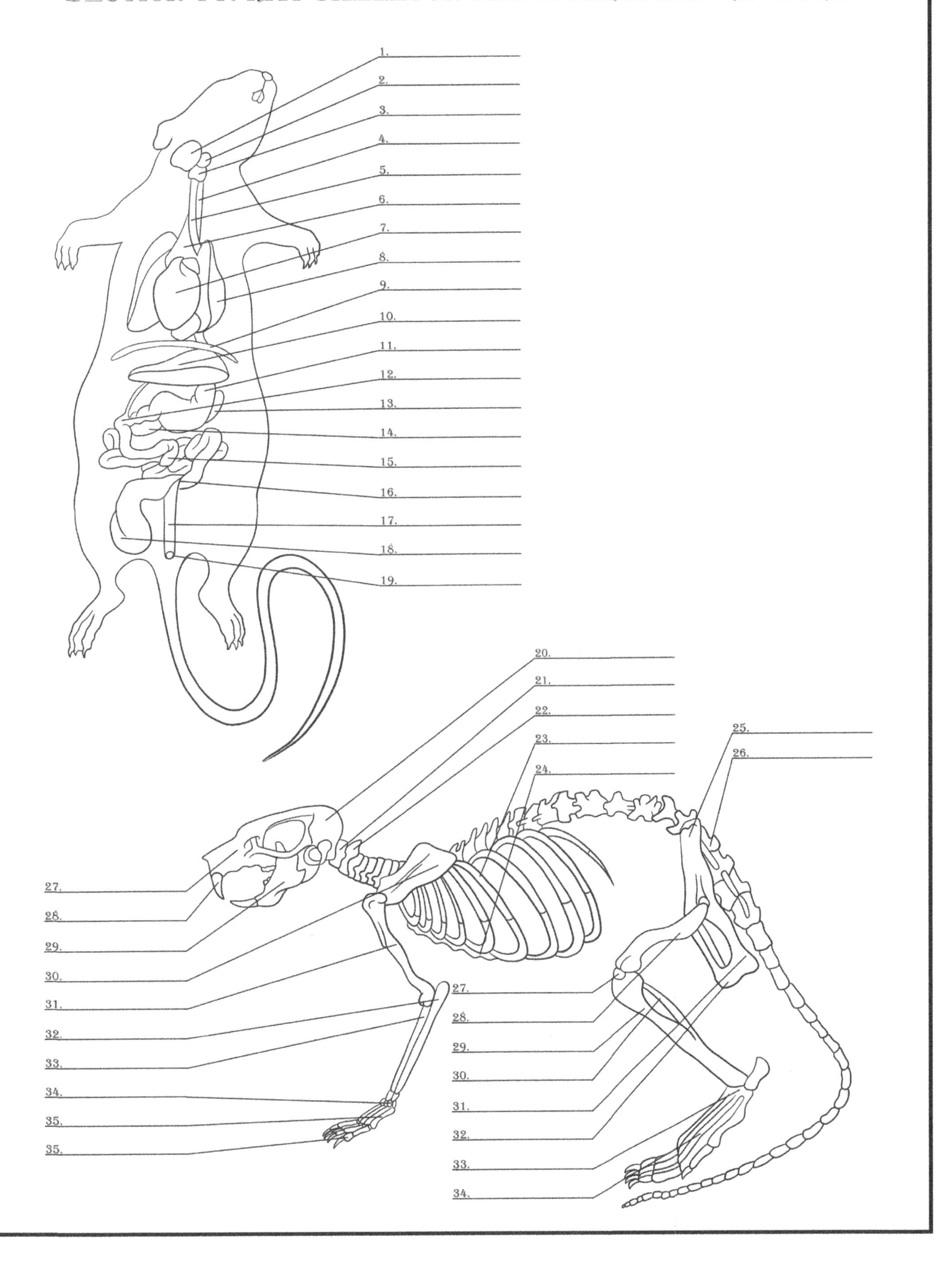

SECTION 11: RAT SKELETON AND INTERNAL STRUCTURE

1. SUBMAXILLARY SALIVARY GLAND
2. LARYNX
3. THYROID GLAND
4. ESOPHAGUS
5. TRACHEA
6. THYMUS GLAND
7. HEART
8. LUNG
9. DIAPHRAGM
10. LIVER
11. STOMACH
12. DUODENUM
13. SPLEEN
14. PANCREAS
15. ILEUM
16. DESCENDING COLON
17. RECTUM
18. CECUM
19. ANUS
20. SKULL
21. ATLAS
22. AXIS
23. RIB
24. STERNUM
25. ILIUM
26. SACRUM
27. PATELLA
28. FEMUR
29. TIBIA
30. FIBULA
31. ISCHIUM
32. PUBIS
33. METATARSAL
34. TARSAL

SECTION 12: RAT MUSCLES AND EXTERNAL STRUCTURE

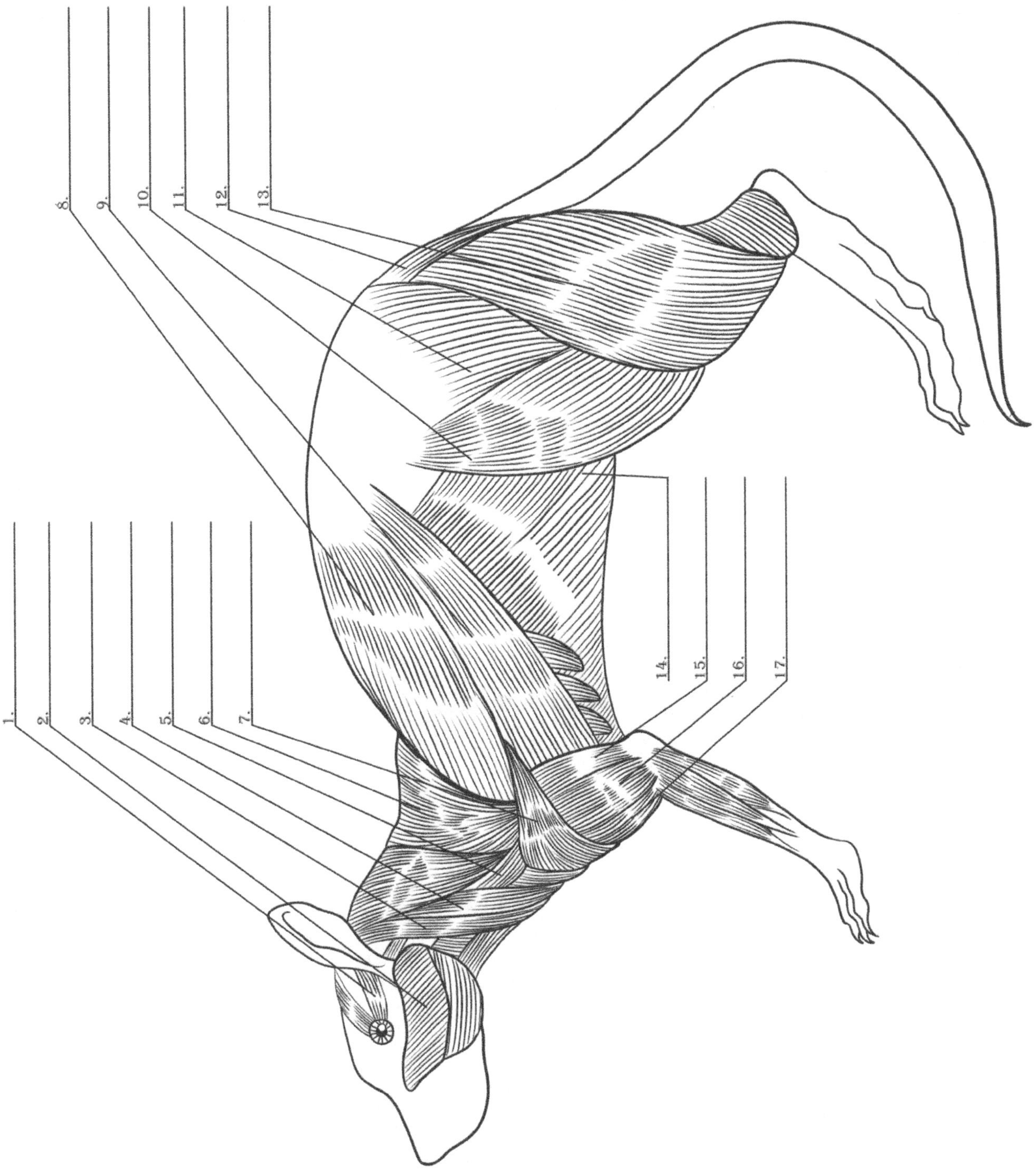

SECTION 12: RAT MUSCLES AND EXTERNAL STRUCTURE

1. TEMPORALIS
2. MASSETER
3. STERNOMASTOIDEUS
4. CLAVOTRAPEZIUS
5. LEVATOR SCAPULAE VENTRALIS
6. ACROMIOTRAPEZIUS
7. SPINODELTOIDEUS
8. SPINOTRAPEZIUS
9. LATISSIMUS DORSI
10. TENSOR FASCIAE LATAE
11. GLUTEUS MAXIMUS
12. SEMITENDINOSUS
13. BICEPS FEMORIS
14. EXTERNAL OBLIQUE
15. TRICEPS
16. BRACHIALIS
17. BICEPS

SECTION 12: RAT MUSCLES AND EXTERNAL STRUCTURE

SECTION 12: RAT MUSCLES AND EXTERNAL STRUCTURE

1. TEMPORALIS
2. MASSETER
3. STERNOMASTOIDEUS
4. CLAVOTRAPEZIUS
5. LEVATOR SCAPULAE VENTRALIS
6. ACROMIOTRAPEZIUS
7. SPINODELTOIDEUS
8. SPINOTRAPEZIUS
9. LATISSIMUS DORSI
10. TENSOR FASCIAE LATAE
11. GLUTEUS MAXIMUS
12. SEMITENDINOSUS
13. BICEPS FEMORIS
14. EXTERNAL OBLIQUE
15. TRICEPS
16. BRACHIALIS
17. BICEPS

SECTION 13: RABBIT SKELETON AND INTERNAL STRUCTURE

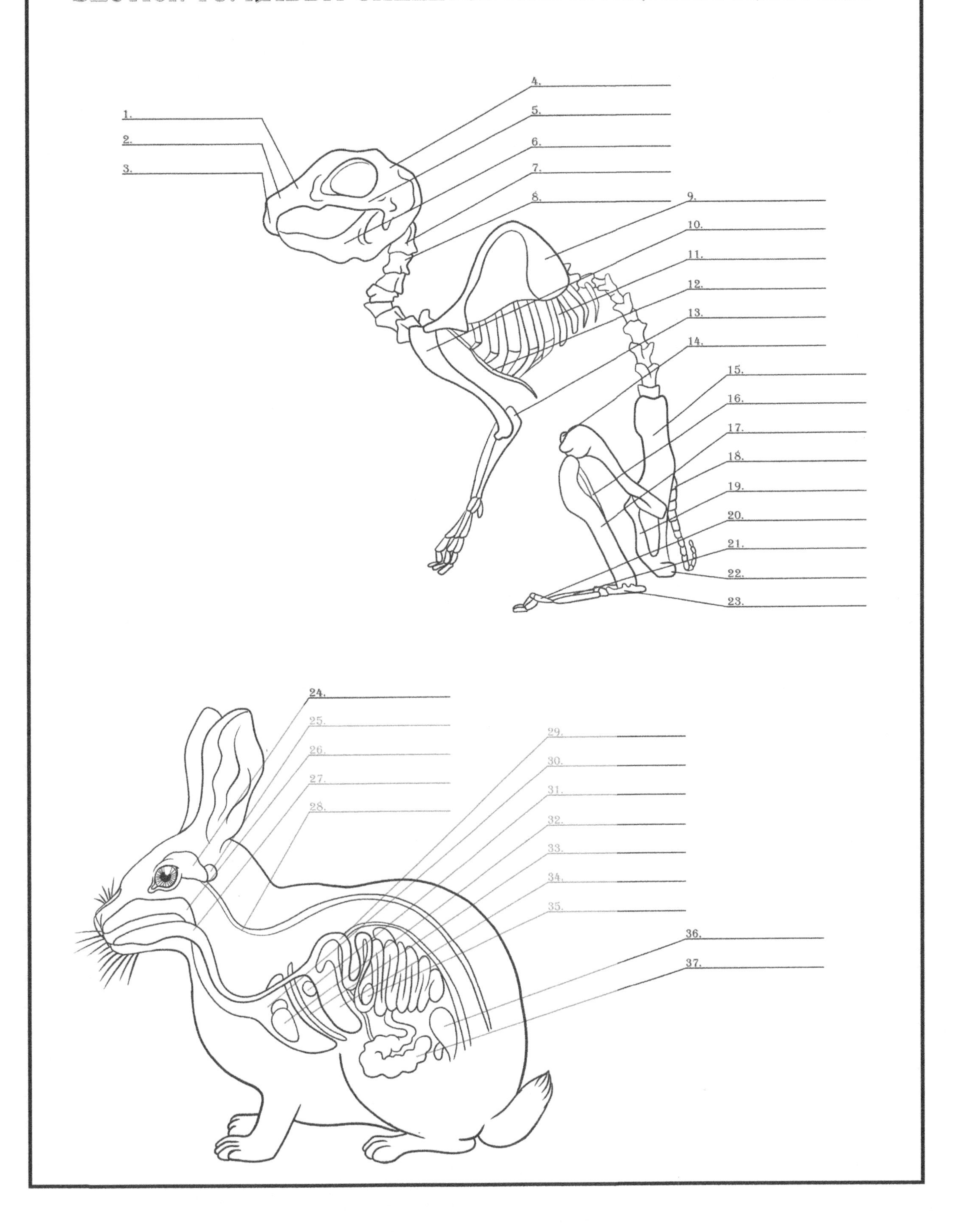

SECTION 13: RABBIT SKELETON AND INTERNAL STRUCTURE

1. MAXILLA
2. NASAL
3. INCISOR
4. SKULL
5. ZYGOMATIC ARCH
6. MANDIBLE
7. ATLAS
8. AXIS
9. SCAPULA
10. HUMERUS
11. RIB
12. STERUM
13. ULNA
14. PATELLA
15. ILIUM
16. FIBULA
17. TIBIA
18. SACRUM
19. PUBIS
20. PHALANGE
21. METATARSAL
22. ISCHIUM
23. TARSAL
24. CEREBRUM
25. CEREBELLUM
26. TRACHEA
27. ESOPHAGUS
28. SPINAL CORD
29. LUNG
30. DUODENUM
31. GALL BLADDER
32. HEART
33. DIAPHRAGM
34. STOMACH
35. PANCREAS
36. BLADDER
37. CECUM

SECTION 14: RABBIT MUSCLES AND EXTERNAL STRUCTURE

SECTION 14: RABBIT MUSCLES AND EXTERNAL STRUCTURE

1. TEMPORALIS
2. ORBICULARIS OCULI
3. MASSETER
4. MALARIA
5. BUCCINATOR
6. ZYGOMATICUS
7. ORBICULARIS ORIS
8. SPLENIUS
9. STERNOHYOID
10. STERNOMASTOIDEUS
11. CLEIDOMASTOID
12. TRAPEZIUS
13. SUPRASPINATUS
14. DELTOID
15. INFRASPINATUSM
16. TRAPEZIUS
17. LATISSIMUS DORSI
18. TENSOR FASCIAE LATAE
19. RECTUS FEMORIS
20. GLUTEUS
21. BICEPS FEMORIS
22. SBMIMEMBRANOSUS
23. COCCYGEUS
24. SEMITENDINOSUS
25. BRACHIOCEPHALICUS
26. TRICEPS BRACHII
27. BRACHIALIS
28. RECTUS ABDOMINIS
29. EXTENSOR CARPI RADIALIS

SECTION 15: CANINE SKELETON AND INTERNAL STRUCTURE

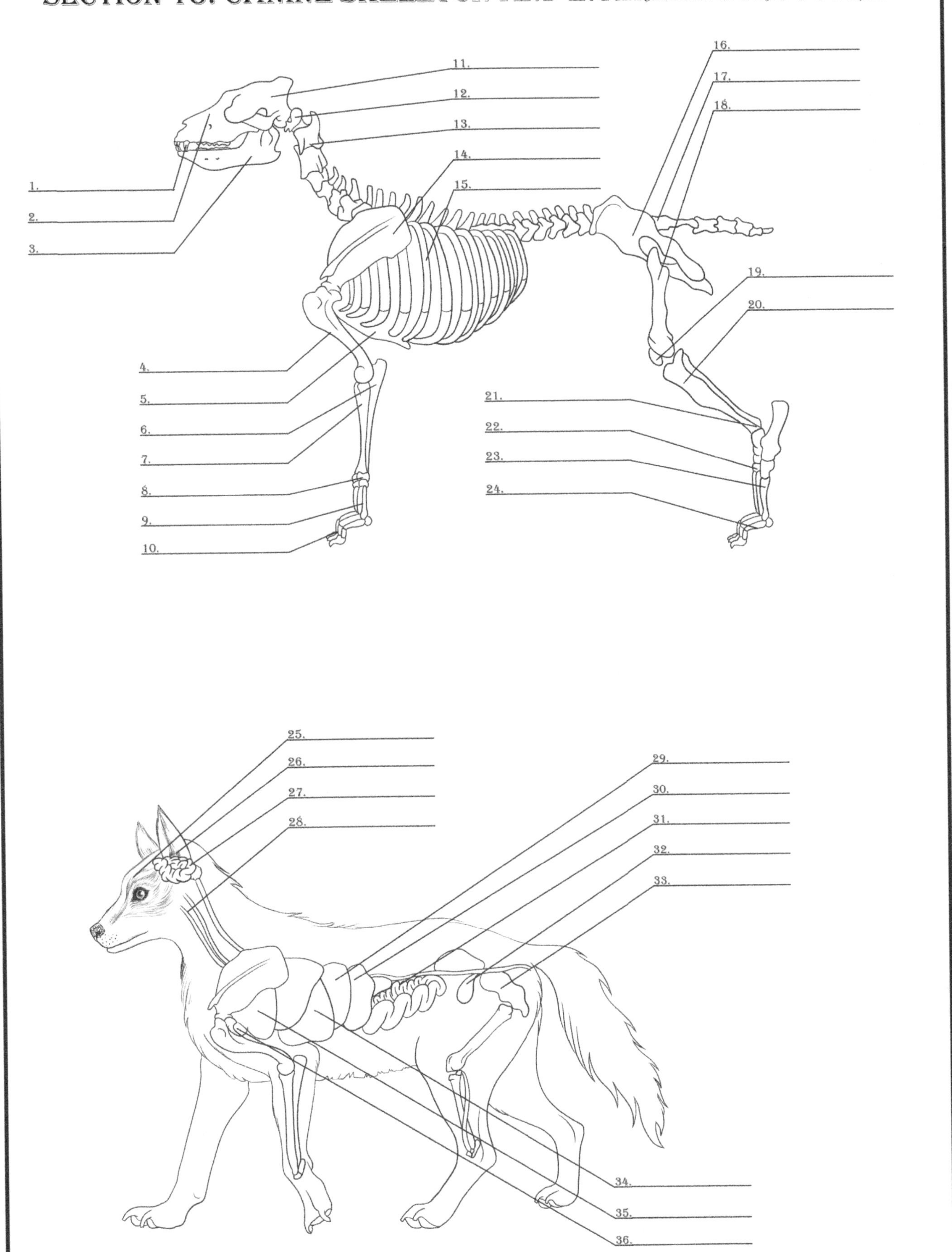

SECTION 15: CANINE SKELETON AND INTERNAL STRUCTURE

1. CANINE TOOTH
2. UPPER JAW
3. LOWER JAW
4. HUMERUS
5. STERNUM
6. ULNA
7. RADIUS
8. CARPUS
9. METACARPUS
10. CLAW
11. SKULL
12. ATLAS
13. AXIS
14. SCAPULA
15. RIB
16. PELVIS
17. SACRUM
18. FEMUR
19. PATELLA
20. TIBIA
21. FIBULA
22. TARSUS
23. METATARSUS
24. PHALANGE
25. NASAL CAVITY
26. CEREBRUM
27. CEREBELLUM
28. ESOPHAGUS
29. STOMACH
30. SPLEEN
31. INTESTINE
32. BLADDER
33. RECTUM
34. LIVER
35. LUNG
36. HEART

SECTION 16: CANINE MUSCLES

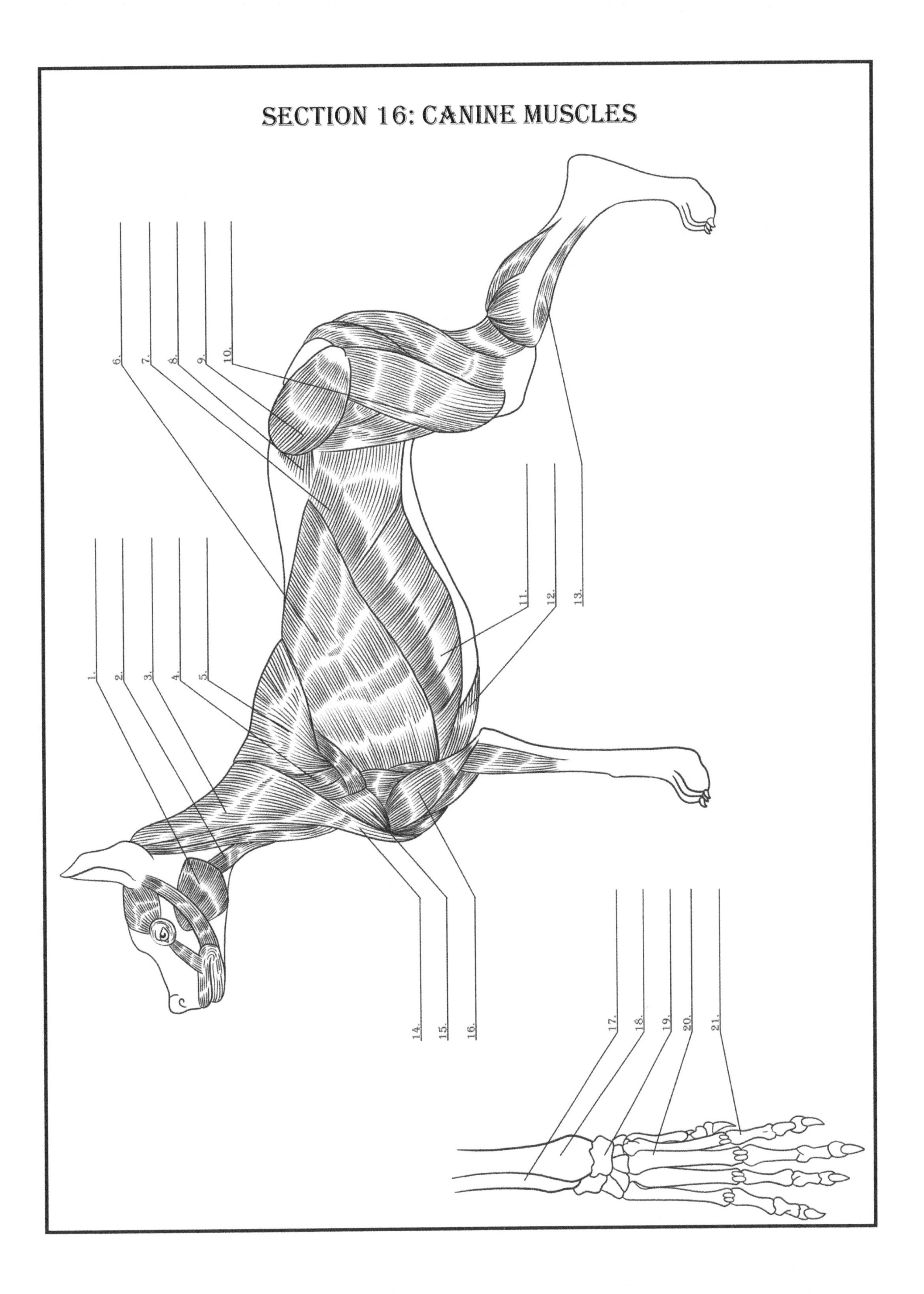

SECTION 16: CANINE MUSCLES

1. MASSETER
2. STERNOHYOID
3. BRACHIOCEPHALICUS
4. OMOTRANSVERSARIUS
5. TRAPEZIUS
6. LATISSIMUS DORSI
7. OBLIQUUS EXTERNUS ABDOMINIS
8. OBLIQUUS INTERNUS ABDOMINIS
9. GLUTEUS MEDIUS
10. BICEPS FEMORIS
11. INTERCOSTALIS EXTERNUS
12. PECTORALIS PROFUNDUS
13. CRANIAL TIBIAL
14. CLAVICULAR TENDINOUS SEPTUM
15. DELTOIDEUS
16. TRICEPS BRACHII
17. ULNA
18. RADIUS
19. CARPAL
20. METACARPAL
21. DIGIT

SECTION 17: FELINE SKELETON AND INTERNAL STRUCTURE

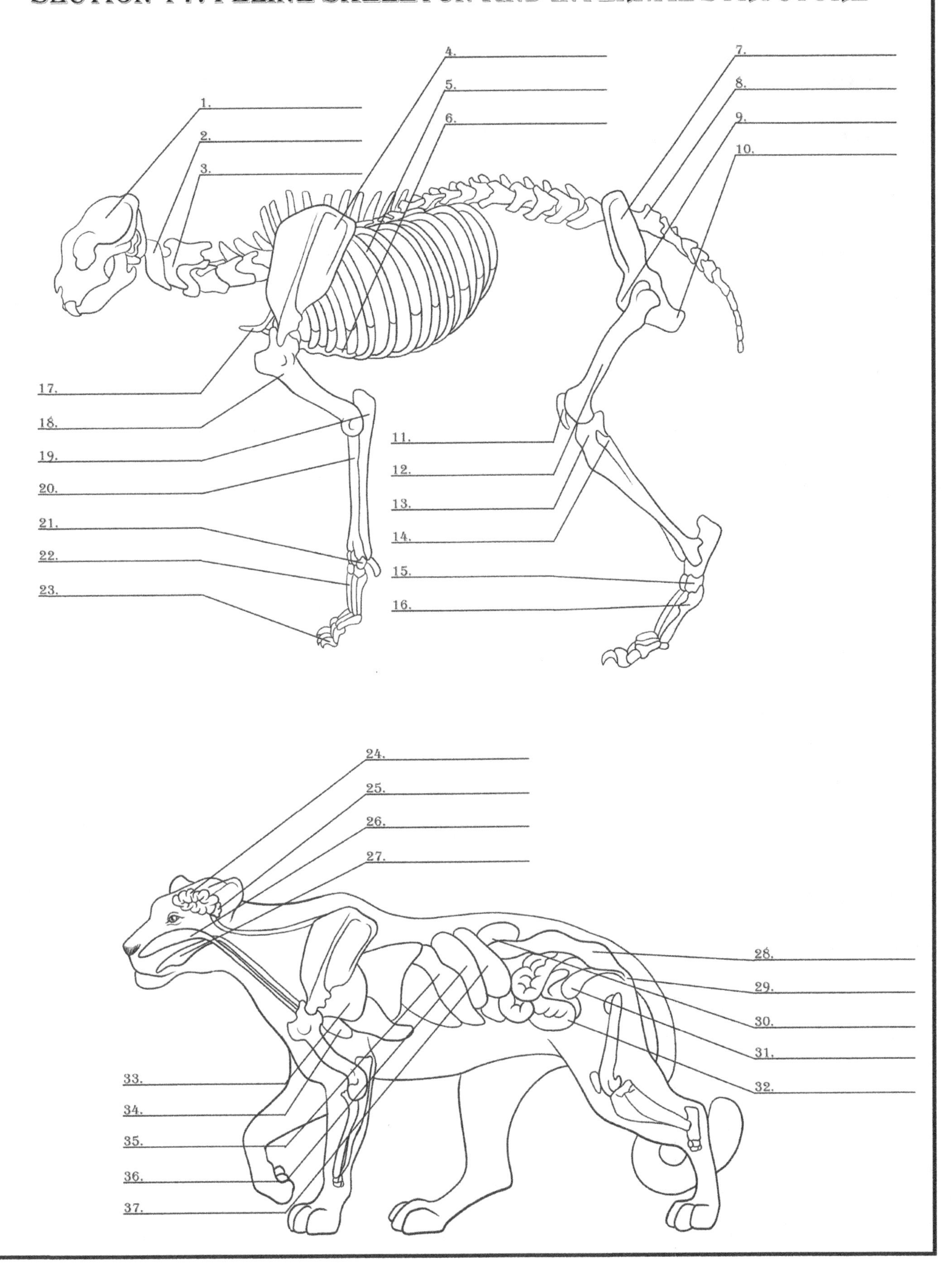

SECTION 17: FELINE SKELETON AND INTERNAL STRUCTURE

1. SKULL
2. ATLAS
3. AXIS
4. SCAPULA
5. RIB
6. STERNUM
7. HIP BONE
8. SACRUM
9. PUBIC BONE
10. ISCHIAL BONE
11. PATELLA
12. FEMUR
13. TIBIA
14. FIBULA
15. TARSAL
16. METATARSAK
17. CLAVICLE
18. HUMERUS
19. ULNA
20. RADIUS
21. CARPAL
22. METACARPAL
23. CLAW
24. CEREBRUM
25. CEREBELLUM
26. NASAL CAVITY
27. TONGUE
28. COLON
29. ANUS
30. BLADDER
31. KIDNEY
32. SMALL INTESTINE
33. LUNG
34. HEART
35. LIVER
36. STOMACH
37. SPLEEN

SECTION 18: FELINE MUSCLES

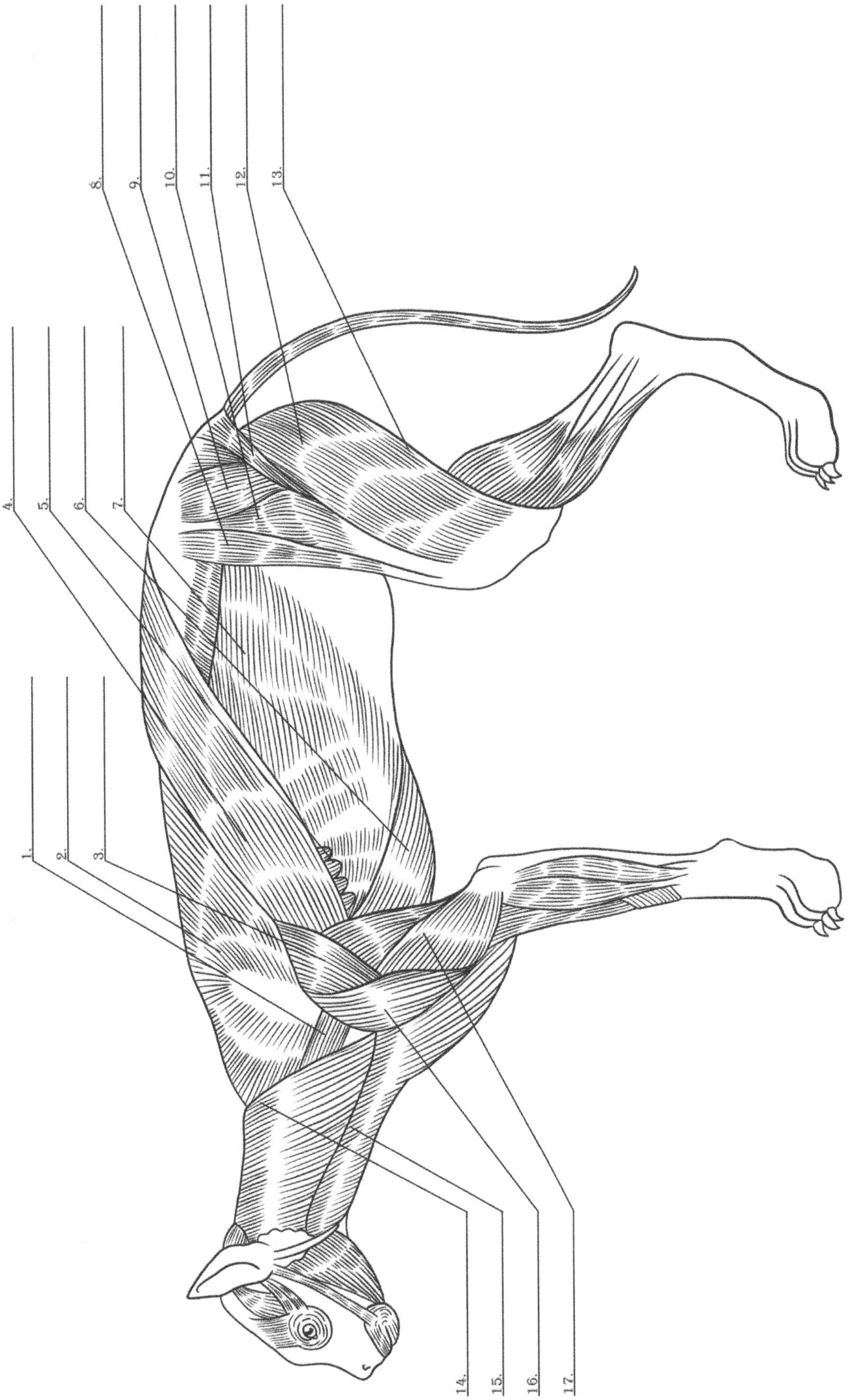

1.
2.
3.
4.
5.
6.
7.
8.
9.
10.
11.
12.
13.
14.
15.
16.
17.

SECTION 18: FELINE MUSCLES

1. OMOTRANSVERSARIUS
2. TRAPEZIUS
3. INFRASPINATUS
4. LATISSIMUS DORSI
5. SERRATUS VENTRALIS
6. PECTORALIS PROFUNDUS
7. EXTERNAL OBLIQUE ABDOMINAL
8. SARTORIUS
9. GLUTEUS MEDIUS
10. TENSOR FASCIAE LATAE
11. CAUDOFEMORALIS
12. BICEPS FEMORIS
13. SEMITENDINOSUS
14. BRACHIOCEPHALICUS
15. STERNOCEPHALICUS
16. DELTOIDEUS
17. TRICEPS BRACHII

SECTION 19: SHEEP SKELETON AND INTERNAL STRUCTURE

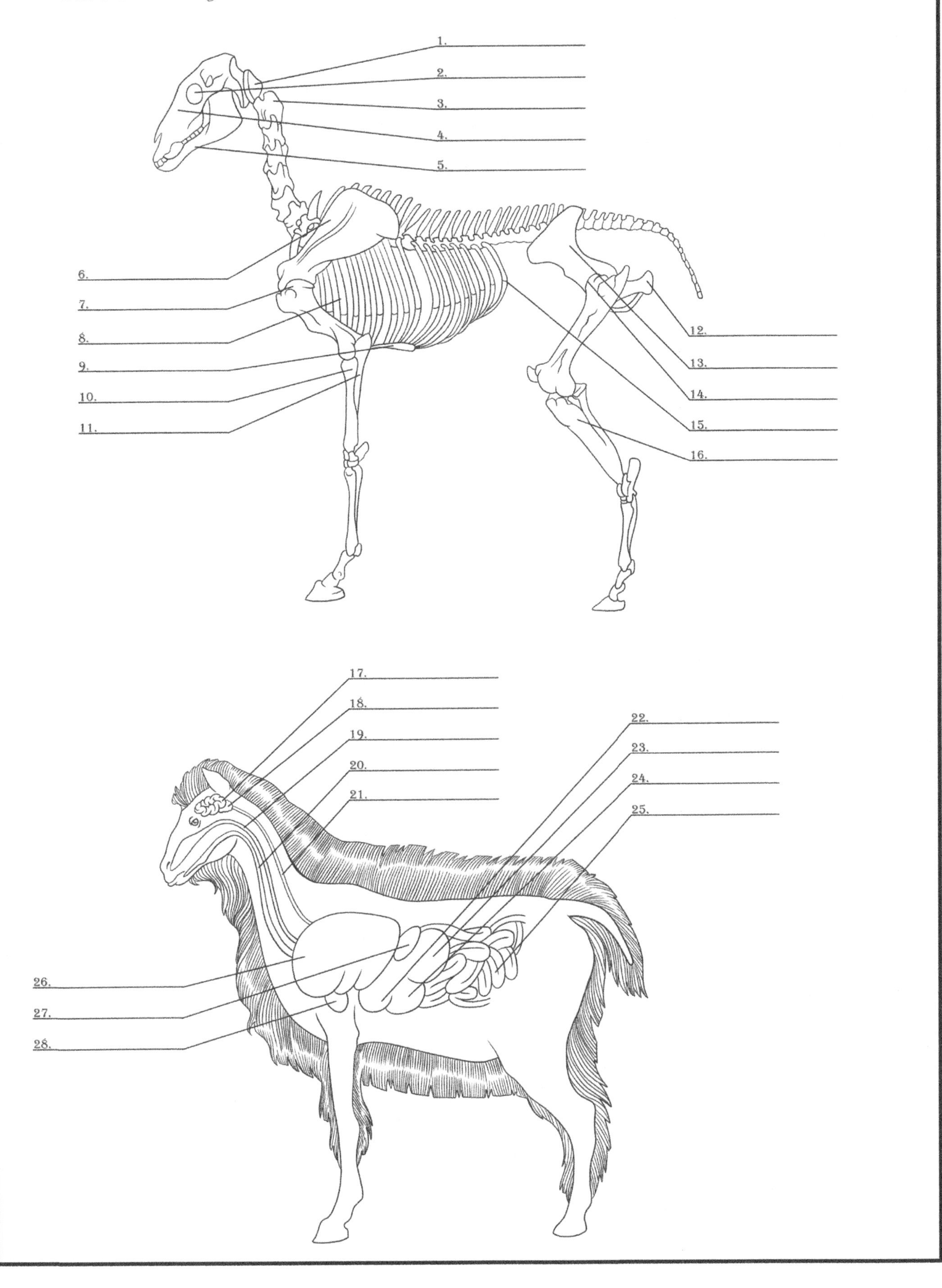

SECTION 19: SHEEP SKELETON AND INTERNAL STRUCTURE

1. ATLAS
2. ORBIT
3. AXIS
4. MAXILLA
5. MANDIBLE
6. SCAPULA
7. HUMERUS
8. RIB
9. STERNUM
10. RADIUS
11. ULNA
12. ISCHIAL TUBER
13. PELVIS
14. HIP JOINT
15. COSTAL ARCH, THE KNEE OF THE RIB
16. TIBIA
17. CEREBRUM
18. CEREBELLUM
19. TRACHEA
20. ESOPHAGUS
21. SPINAL CORD
22. ABOMASUM
23. DORSAL SAC OF RUMEN
24. VENTRAL SAC OF RUMEN
25. SMALL INTESTINE
26. LUNG
27. SPLEEN
28. HEART

SECTION 20: SHEEP MUSCLES

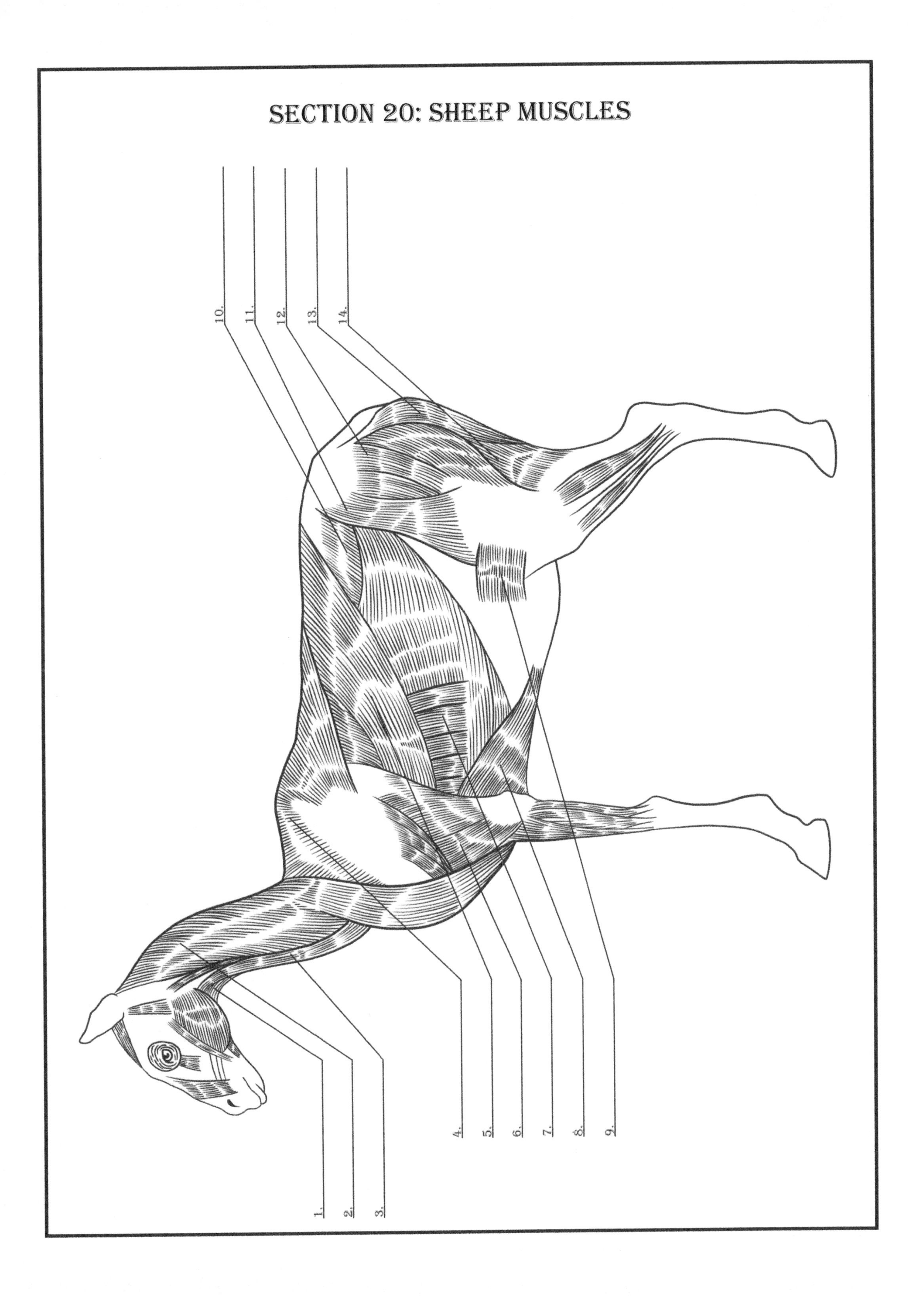

SECTION 20: SHEEP MUSCLES

1. STERNOHYOIDEUS
2. BRACHIOCEPHALICUS
3. STERNOCEPHALICUS
4. TRAPEZIUS
5. LATISSIMUS DORSI
6. TRICEPS BRACHII
7. SERRATUS VENTRALIS
8. PECTORALIS PROFUNDUS
9. CUTANEUS PLICAE
10. OBLIQUUS INTERNUS ABDOMINIS
11. TENSOR FASCIAE LATAE
12. GLUTEUS PROXIMALIS
13. SEMITENDINOSUS
14. GLUTEOBICEPS

SECTION 21: PIG SKELETON AND INTERNAL STRUCTURE

1. ______________________
2. ______________________
3. ______________________
4. ______________________
5. ______________________
6. ______________________
7. ______________________
8. ______________________
9. ______________________
10. ______________________
11. ______________________
12. ______________________
13. ______________________
14. ______________________
15. ______________________
16. ______________________
17. ______________________
18. ______________________
19. ______________________
20. ______________________
21. ______________________
22. ______________________
23. ______________________
24. ______________________
25. ______________________
26. ______________________
27. ______________________
28. ______________________
29. ______________________
30. ______________________
31. ______________________
32. ______________________
33. ______________________

SECTION 21: PIG SKELETON AND INTERNAL STRUCTURE

1. SKULL
2. OCCIPITAL CREST
3. MAXILLA
4. ATLAS
5. AXIS
6. PELVIS
7. SACRUM
8. FEMUR
9. MANDIBLE
10. SCAPULA
11. HUMERUS
12. RIB
13. STERNUM
14. RADIUS
15. ULNA
16. CARPAL
17. METACARPAL
18. PATELLA
19. TIBIA
20. FIBULA
21. CEREBRUM
22. CEREBELLUM
23. SPINAL CORD
24. TRACHEA
25. KIDNEY
26. SPLEEN
27. RECTUM
28. SMALL INTESTINE
29. LUNG
30. HEART
31. STOMACH
32. LIVER
33. BLADDER

SECTION 22: PIG MUSCLES

1.
2.
3.
4.
5.
6.
7.
8.
9.
10.
11.
12.
13.
14.
15.
16.
17.
18.
19.
20.
21.
22.
23.
24.

SECTION 22: PIG MUSCLES

1. BRACHIOCEPHALICUS
2. PAROTIDEOAURICULARIS
3. STERNOHYOIDEUS
4. TRAPEZIUS
5. DELTOIDEUS
6. TRICEPS BRACHII
7. LATISSIMUS DORSI
8. SERRATUS DORSALIS
9. OBLIQUUS EXTERNUS ABDOMINIS
10. TENSOR FASCIAE LATAE
11. GLUTEUS MEDIUS
12. GLUTEUS SUPERFICIALIS
13. BICEPS FEMORIS
14. SEMITENDINOSUS
15. DIGITAL CUSHION
16. SOLE
17. BORDER OF THE SOLE
18. REGION OF THE FETLOCK JOINTS
19. REGION OF THE PASTERN JOINTS
20. DEWCLAW
21. PALMAR/PLANTAR BORDER OF THE HORNY WALL
22. THE TIP OF THE HORNY WALL
23. PERIOPLE
24. CORONET REGION

SECTION 23: HORSE SKELETON AND INTERNAL STRUCTURE

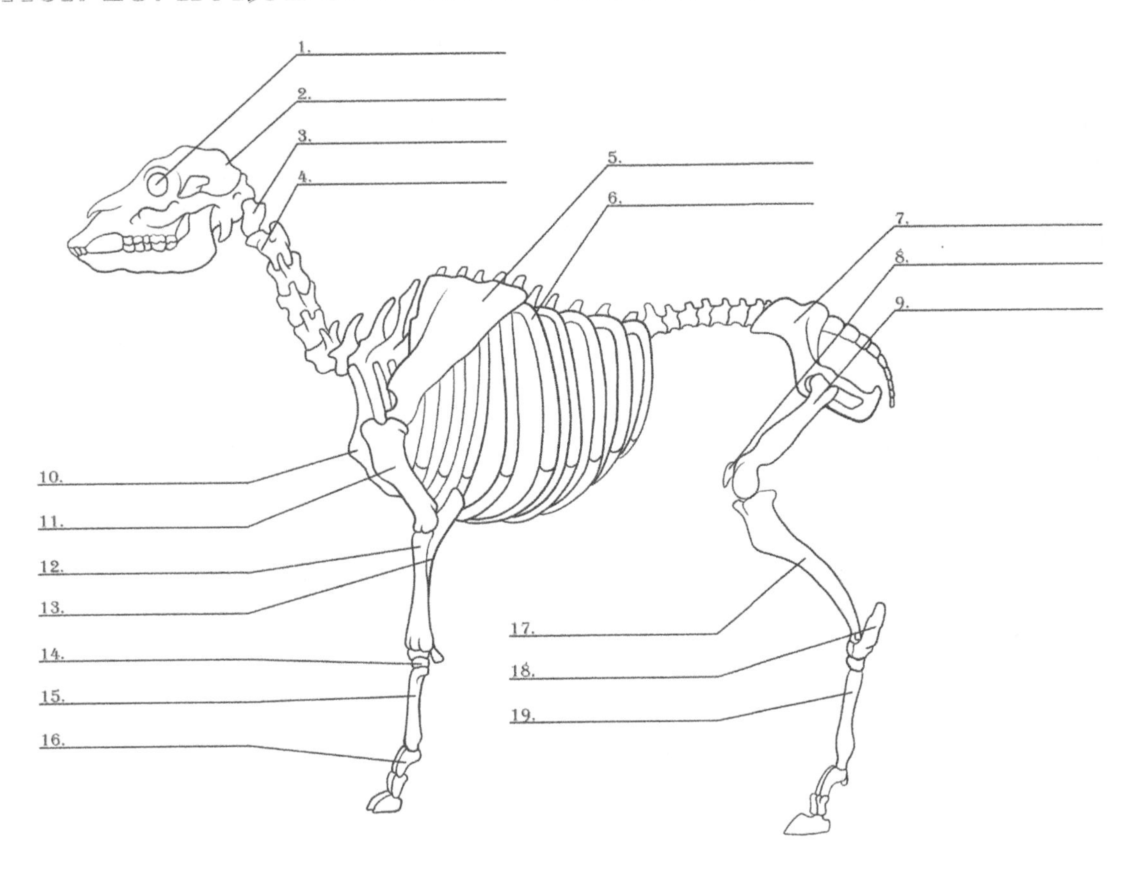

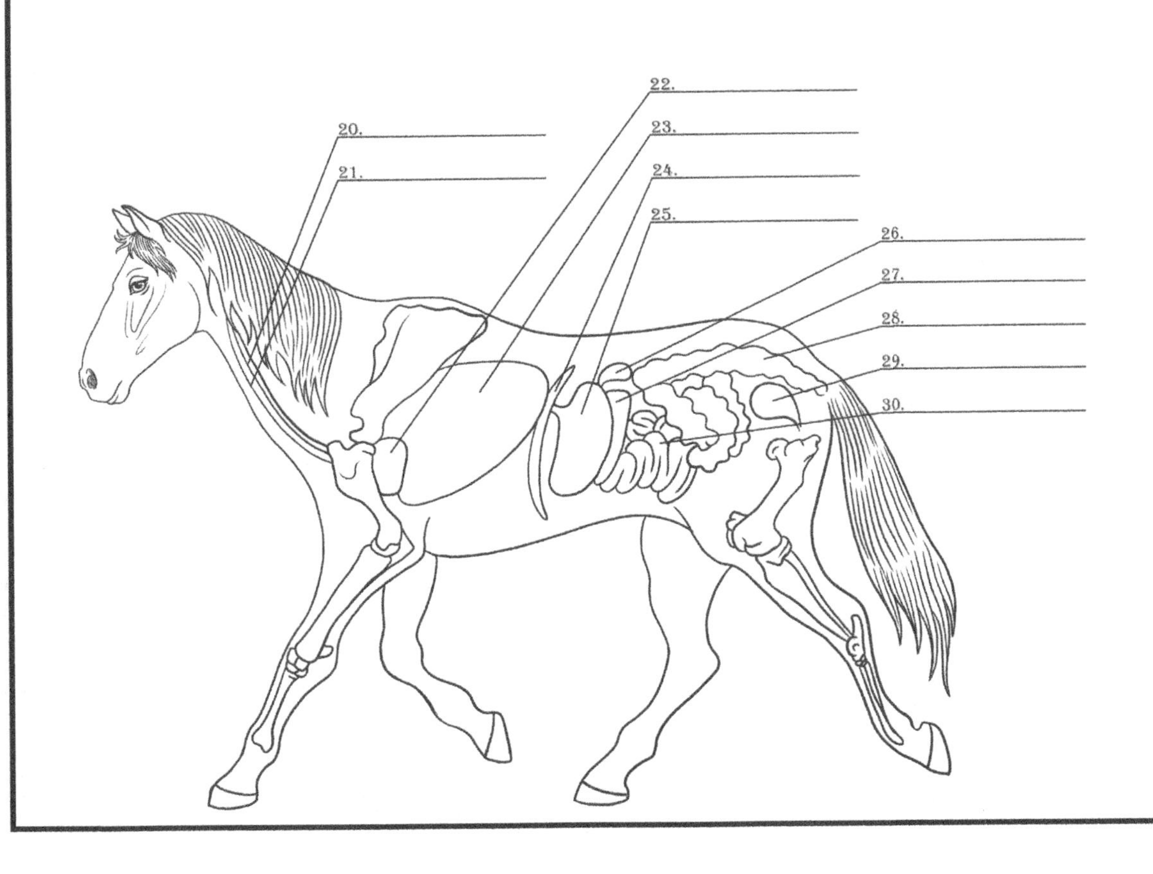

SECTION 23: HORSE SKELETON AND INTERNAL STRUCTURE

1. ORBIT
2. SKULL
3. ATLAS
4. AXIS
5. SCAPULA
6. RIB
7. PELVIS
8. PATELLA
9. FEMUR
10. STERNUM
11. HUMERUS
12. RADIUS
13. ULNA
14. CARPAL
15. METACARPAL
16. PHALANGE
17. TIBIA
18. CALCANEOUS
19. METATARSAL
20. TRACHEA
21. ESOPHAGUS
22. HEART
23. LUNG
24. DIAPHRAGM
25. STOMACH
26. KIDNEY
27. SPLEEN
28. RECTUM
29. BLADDER
30. SMALL INTESTINE

SECTION 24: HORSE MUSCLES

1.
2.
3.
4.
5.
6.
7.
8.
9.
10.
11.
12.
13.
14.
15.
16.
17.
18.
19.
20.
21.
22.
23.
24.
25.
26.
27.
28.
29.
30.
31.
32.
33.

SECTION 24: HORSE MUSCLES

1. ORBICULARIS OCULI
2. TEMPORALIS
3. MASSETER
4. CERVICAL RHOMBOIDEUS
5. SPLENIUS
6. STERNOCEPHALICUS
7. BRACHIOCEPHALICUS
8. TRAPEZIUS
9. EXTERNAL INTERCOSTAL
10. EXTERNAL ABDOMINAL OBLIQUE
11. GLUTEAL FASCIA
12. TENSOR FASCIAE LATAE
13. GLUTEUS SUPERFICIALIS
14. BICEPS FEMORIS
15. SEMITENDINOSUS
16. DELTOIDEUS
17. TRICEPS BRACHII
18. EXTENSOR CARPI RADIALIS
19. PECTORALIS
20. TRICEPS
21. EXTENSOR CARPI ULNARIS
22. RADIUS
23. CARPUS
24. SPLINT BONE
25. METACARPAL (CANNON BONE)
26. PROXIMAL SESAMOIDS
27. METACARPAL-PHALANGAL (FETLOCK) JOINT
28. PROXIMAL PHALANX
29. MIDDLE PHALANX
30. DISTAL PHALANX
31. FLEXOR DIGITORUM PROFUNDUS
32. EXTENSOR DIGITORUM LATERALIS
33. EXTENSOR DIGITORUM LONGUS

SECTION 25: COW SKELETON AND INTERNAL STRUCTURE

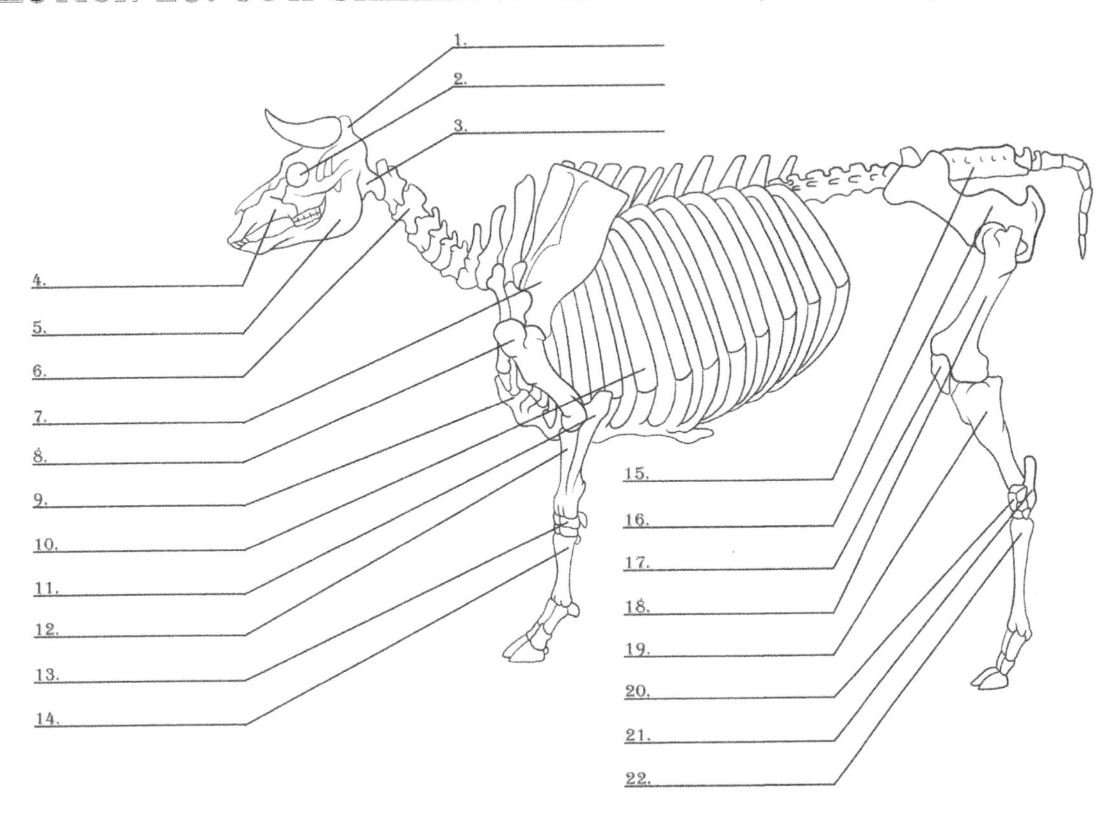

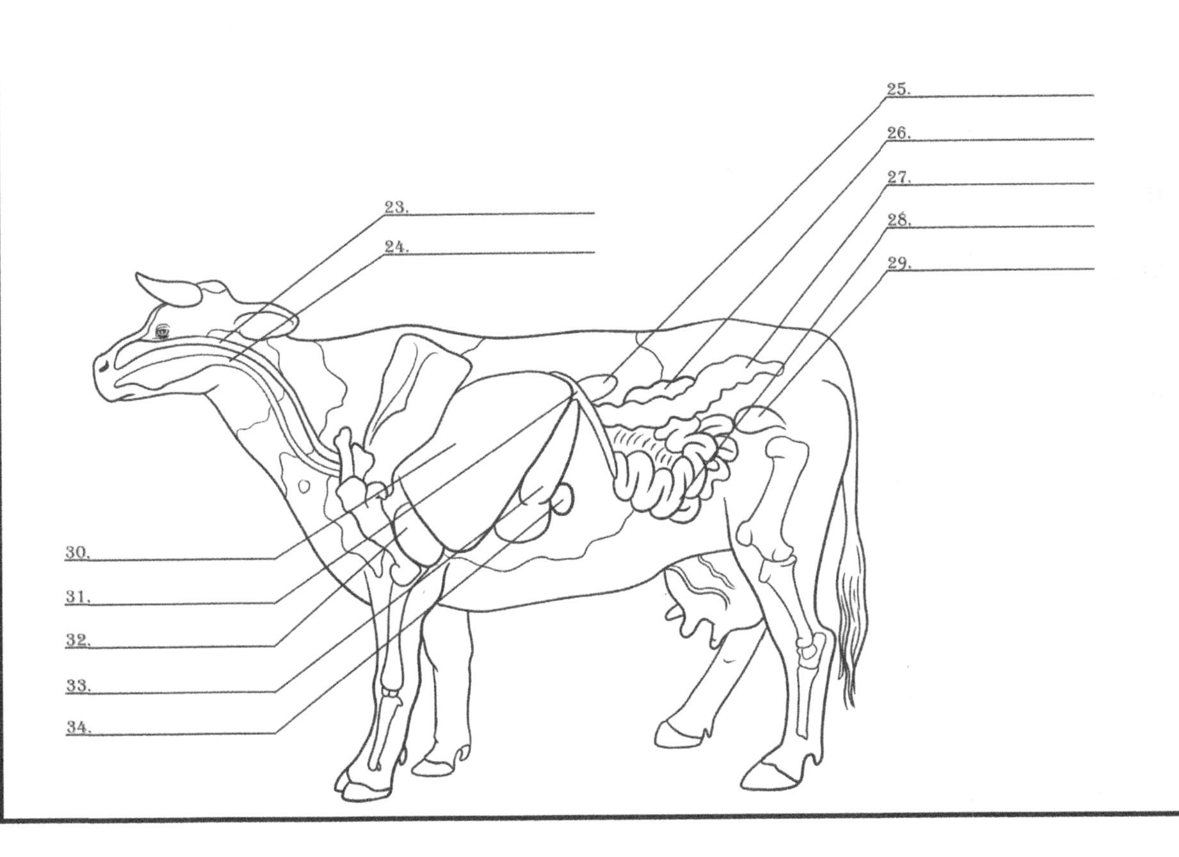

SECTION 25: COW SKELETON AND INTERNAL STRUCTURE

1. CORNUAL PROCESS OF THE FRONTAL BONE
2. ORBIT
3. ATLAS
4. MAXILLA
5. MANDIBLE
6. AXIS
7. SCAPULA
8. HUMERUS
9. STERNUM
10. RIB
11. ULNA
12. RADIUS
13. CARPUS
14. METACARPUS
15. SACRUM
16. PELVIS
17. PATELLA
18. FEMUR
19. TIBIA
20. TARSAL
21. CALCANEAL TTUBEROSITY
22. METATARSUS
23. TRACHEA
24. ESOPHAGUS
25. KIDNEY
26. DUODENUM
27. CECUM
28. JEJUNUM
29. BLADDER
30. LUNG
31. DIAPHRAGM
32. HEART
33. LIVER
34. GALL BLADDER

SECTION 26: COW MUSCLES

SECTION 26: COW MUSCLES

1. ORBICULARIS OCULI
2. MASSETER
3. ZYGOMATIC
4. STERNOMANDIBULARIS
5. TRAPEZIUS
6. CLEIDOMASTOIDEUS
7. BRACHIOCEPHALICUS
8. GLUTEUS PROXIMAL
9. SERRATUS VENTRALIS
10. OBLIQUUS EXTERNUS ABDOMINIS
11. TENSOR FASCIAE LATAE
12. GLUTEUS PROXIMALIS
13. YELLOW ABDOMINAL FASCIA (TUNICA FLAVA ABDOMINIS)
14. STIFLE JOINT
15. GLUTEUS CAUDALIS
16. PECTORALIS
17. TUBER OLECRANI WITH THE TRICEPS BRACHII MUSCLE
18. PECTORALIS
19. RADIUS
20. CARPUS
21. SPLINT BONE
22. METACARPAL (CANNON) BONE
23. PROXIMAL SESAMOIDS
24. METACARPAL-PHALANGAL (FETLOCK) JOINT
25. PROXIMAL PHALANX
26. MIDDLE PHALANX
27. DISTAL PHALANX

SECTION 27: ELEPHANT SKELETON AND INTERNAL STRUCTURE

1. ____________
2. ____________
3. ____________
4. ____________
5. ____________
6. ____________
7. ____________
8. ____________
9. ____________
10. ____________
11. ____________
12. ____________
13. ____________
14. ____________
15. ____________
16. ____________
17. ____________
18. ____________
19. ____________
20. ____________
21. ____________
22. ____________
23. ____________
24. ____________
25. ____________
26. ____________
27. ____________
28. ____________
29. ____________
30. ____________
31. ____________
32. ____________
33. ____________
34. ____________
35. ____________
36. ____________
37. ____________
38. ____________
39. ____________
40. ____________
41. ____________
42. ____________
43. ____________
44. ____________
45. ____________
46. ____________
47 ____________

SECTION 27: ELEPHANT SKELETON AND INTERNAL STRUCTURE

1. SKULL
2. ROSTRAL BONE
3. TEMPORAL FOSSA
4. ORBITAL RIDGE
5. INCISOR (TRUNK SUPPORT)
6. SCAPULA
7. SCAPULAR SPINE
8. RIB
9. MANDIBLE
10. ZYGOMATIC ARCH
11. EAR OPENING
12. HUMERUS
13. STERNUM
14. OLECRANON
15. RADIUS
16. ULNA
17. CARPAL
18. METACARPAL
19. PHALANGE
20. PELVIS
21. SACRUM
22. FEMUR
23. PATELLA
24. TIBIA
25. FIBULA
26. CALCANEUS
27. TARSAL
28. METATARSAL
29. EAR
30. BRAIN
31. TONGUE
32. TRUNK
33. HEART
34. LUNG
35. DIAPHRAGM
36. SPINAL CORD
37. ESOPHAGUS
38. TRACHEA
39. KIDNEY
40. URETER
41. BLADDER
42. DUODENUM
43. SMALL INTESTINE
44. CECUM
45. ANUS
46. SPLEEN
47. STOMACH

SECTION 28: ELEPHANT MUSCLES

1. ___
2. ___
3. ___
4. ___
5. ___
6. ___
7. ___
8. ___
9. ___
10. ___
11. ___
12. ___
13. ___
14. ___
15. ___
16. ___
17. ___
18. ___
19. ___
20. ___
21. ___
22. ___
23. ___
24. ___
25. ___
26. ___
27. ___
28. ___
29. ___
30. ___

SECTION 28: ELEPHANT MUSCLES

1. TRAPEZIUS
2. RHOMBOID
3. SPLENIUS
4. OCCIPITO-FRONTALIS
5. OMOTRANSVERSARIUS
6. TEMPORALIS
7. BRACHIOCEPHALICUS
8. MASSETER
9. ORBICULARIS OCULI
10. BUCCINATOR, PARS SUPRALABIALIS
11. ORBICULARIS ORIS
12. BUCCINATOR, PARS RIMANA
13. LEVATOR LABII MAXILLARIS
14. LATISSIMUS DORSI
15. LONGISSIMUS DORSI
16. EXTERNAL ABDOMINAL OBLIQUE
17. TENSOR FASCIAE LATAE
18. GLUTEUS MEDICUS
19. GLUTEUS SUPERFICIAL
20. BICEPS FEMORIS
21. SEMITENDINOSUS
22. EXTENSOR LATERALIS
23. TIBIALIS CRANIALIS
24. DELTOID, ACROMIAL PORTION
25. DELTOID, SCAPULAR PORTION
26. TRICEPS
27. BRACHIORADIALIS
28. RECTUS ABDOMINALIS
29. EXTENSOR DIGITORUM COMMUNIS
30. ULNARIS